To

Professor and Mrs. Irving Fisher
with the affectionate regards
of t̲h̲e̲ ̲a̲u̲t̲h̲o̲r̲

Léon

New Haven, Ct.
Feb. 3, 1931.

at
nk:
all

ld
ce

PIGEON
CITY

Grizzle—the finest bird in Pigeon City

PIGEON CITY

By
Leon F. Whitney

ROBERT M. McBRIDE & COMPANY
NEW YORK   1931

PIGEON CITY
PRINTED IN THE UNITED STATES OF AMERICA

CONTENTS

ILLUSTRATIONS

FOREWORD

IF I were a boy again—or even a girl—I know of no book about life and nature that I would rather read than "Pigeon City." I wish every boy in America could read it, and every girl, too. It is written by a man who has some fine children of his own and who knows more about children and pigeons and dogs and 'coons and rabbits and animals generally than any one I know. Children miss a whole world if they miss knowing the lives of birds and animals. Mr. Whitney brings one part of this world of nature to them in his delightful book.

So my heart's blessing goes with this book to boys and girls everywhere, for it is written especially for you by one of your best and wisest friends.

Affectionately yours,

ALBERT EDWARD WIGGAM.

PIGEON
CITY

PIGEON CITY

Chapter I

A STREAK IN THE BLUE

"THERE comes one!"

"Where?"

"Just over the top of that tallest smoke-stack, 'way up high."

"I can't see him yet."

"Look sharp! Don't miss it. Oh, boy, it's great. Keep looking just where I said. It's bigger now, but still just a dot. There!"

"Oh, now I see, and I see another too."

"Where?"

"Over the top of that flagpole on the left. See?"

"Gosh, two home already! That's quick, sooner than we thought!"

Up on top of a city-block house in that part of Greater New York known as Brooklyn, looking out of the opening on the southwest side of a funny-looking little shanty, were two boys, Bud and Dick. The housetop was

I

almost flat save for a slight slope which allowed the water to drain off. It was covered with pebbles. Like all other city-block houses it was tight up against the next, and one could walk from one street to the next right over the roofs, stepping or climbing up or down depending on whether the house next door was higher or lower. The boys were on Bud's roof, but Dick lived only two houses away.

The shanty in which they were sitting was not large enough for more than three boys and even then it would have been crowded. It looked much like an old-fashioned cupola on a barn. They had built it themselves in order that they might have a place to sit and watch for the return of their homing pigeons from the races. Now, late in the morning, they were waiting for the return of sixty-two pigeons which had been sent away two hundred miles, together with hundreds of other pigeons all of which had been liberated at seven o'clock that morning.

"Look," said Dick, "one is pretty close now. See, he is drawing in his wings. Press the button."

Bud pressed the button. Immediately a light went on down in a very large pigeon colony three stories lower than where the boys were sitting and at the rear of the back yard.

It was a signal for Bill, the third partner, to
be ready. Birds were coming home, and Bill's
part in the race was an all-important one.
Immediately Bill moved to his post and sat as
still as death—so still indeed that one could
scarcely believe that, within, his heart was
aflutter and his nerves were straining from the
intense excitement.

But on the roof:

"Look, Old Grizzle ahead again!" whispered Bud. "There! look at the old bird
drop! Look at him draw those old wings in
to his sides! Look at him drop!" There was
no time to say more. Grizzle had shot past
them like a streak, now over the roof—down,
down, down, to the colony. He fluttered his
wings vigorously to check the rapid fall,
alighted on the roof, looked about nervously,
pushed his way through the wires of the entrance, dropped down again to another little
enclosure, and there Bill did his work. Deftly
and gently he reached in and taking the old,
experienced bird in his hands, he took from
its leg a small metal band. Putting the pigeon
down again, he straightened out the band and
quickly pushed it into the end of a metal box.
As soon as it was in, he pushed a slide over
the hole and held the box to his ear. It had

been silent, but now the ticking of a clock was to be heard.

Another flickering of the light informed Bill that another bird was nearly there, so he was ready. And again he went through the same performance. By this process he had accurately timed two great homing pigeons.

Then the light flickered three times, meaning that three more birds were soon to alight. So now he took out his watch and a pencil, picked up a pad and sat still. The second bird to come in had been a black one, then came a third, a beautiful red-checked male, then in rapid succession came another red-check, then a blue-check. Again Bill waited and then the light flickered repeatedly for quite a time. And now came a whole flock, twenty-five birds or more, and Bill had his troubles trying to keep track of them in the order in which they popped through the wires. But after the first two, only the names and the time were recorded—these late-comers were not timed in the clocking device.

Bill was having a fine time, but most boys would have chosen to be Bud or Dick. They could sit and watch the little dim specks get larger and larger, see specks which they thought were their own pigeons get larger too, and then pass overhead instead of dropping. These were other boys' or men's pigeons. One after another the specks would grow in size, and finally in most cases turn into homing pigeons which would sometimes pull in their wings and drop down, sometimes fly in circles lower and lower until they were down to their home, and once in a while, to the great annoyance of the boys, alight on the roof of one of the houses in the neighborhood. Poor tired birds, they had flown two hundred miles to get home, and now that they were within sight of it, they were too tired to get down to the water and food—just content to sit and look at their home. Generally these were the younger birds, or those that were not in such good condition. The old and the well-trained and well-conditioned birds dropped immediately down to their home and went in, ate and drank and felt better. And this was lucky for the pigeon fanciers because otherwise they could not have timed their birds accurately, or not accurately enough to satisfy all who were interested in winning a great race.

Few things can give a boy or man a greater thrill than watching the return from a distance of the homing pigeons which he has bred and trained. This was only one of the many races in which the now-famous homers of Pigeon

City had taken part. These birds were known far and wide as the best that flew, and men as well as boys were vying to beat Pigeon City birds in at least one race.

The proprietors of Pigeon City were Bud, Bill and Dick, all handy with tools and fond of pets, boys of whom any father and mother would have been proud. Their parents *were* proud of them! And a lot of boys in the neighborhood were not a little envious of the three. Both of these facts can easily be explained: they usually minded their own business, and they had an object in life—which interested them tremendously.

But to arrive at their present stage of success, the owners of Pigeon City had started many years before to learn all about raising pigeons. Now they were old enough to go to college, all planning to start the next fall. Let us take a look back over the past.

Chapter II

ONE COMMON INTEREST

PARTNERSHIPS are interesting affairs. Have you ever thought just why you are drawn more to some boys you know than to others? If you ever did, you may have realized that before there can be a successful partnership there must be a common interest. It is strange what little things often draw people to each other. In the case of Bud and Dick and Bill it was a common interest in pigeons that made them such staunch friends, and that brought into their early lives such rich experiences.

But before we begin to tell of the exciting and interesting experiences that they were having in their pigeon business now, we must learn something of what the boys had been doing in earlier years. You might think it incredible that such young fellows could train their pigeons to win races, could breed great fliers, could put their birds in competition against those of experienced *men* for the honors of winning. That does sound unreasonable. But when we know that before they ever owned a homer they had gone through the mill, so to speak, that they had learned to know pigeons while they were still quite small boys, then we can readily understand why they were so successful in later years. Experience had been a wise and thorough teacher.

INTRODUCING GEORGE HITCHCOCK

The reason that we ought to get acquainted with Bud first is this: if it had not been for him there might not have been any Pigeon City.

Just ten years before we find the boys watching for the pigeons to return, a blond, curly-headed little shaver was walking along a busy city street holding on to the hand of his grandfather, while they looked at the many interesting objects to be seen in the store windows.

They walked along slowly, and Gramp, as George affectionately called him, stopped to inspect some neckties; next they gazed at the beautiful pictures in an art-store window; a little further on they were attracted by the billboards of a moving-picture theater.

Crossing the next street, they walked on a little way and came to many more interesting windows. Suddenly Gramp felt a vigorous pull at his arm.

"Look, quick!" shouted his eight-year-old companion. "Here's where we can stand and watch for half a day!"

They were standing before the window of a pet shop. There they saw puppies: cute, roly-poly, reddish puppies. They had just been fed and they were romping and pulling each other about. They were so amusing that they held the attention of the old man and the boy for a long while. Then a little monkey began to attract attention to himself. He was up above the pups in a cage. And for some time the two kept their eyes on him. There were lots of other pets, too, including several Angora kittens, and some parakeets that sat close together and looked like the little lovers that they were.

When their interest in this window began to wane, Gramp and Bud drifted over to the other side of the pet-shop door and looked in the second window. It was filled with birds. In the center was a gaudy parrot on a pole with a little chain attached to his leg. In two big cages, below and on either side, were pigeons, and up above in other cages were canaries and doves, and here too were several cages filled with single pairs of pigeons.

"Look, quick! Here's where we can stand and
watch for half a day!"

These seemed to hold the eyes of the visitors even more than the monkey and the dogs had done. George, especially, was fascinated by the big old pouter pigeon with his brown color and the crescent across his crop, the glittering, iridescent gold and green on his neck that changed color as he moved, the enormous balloon that he blew up and deflated, and his proud "Coocutty coooo" to the lady pouter who had no such crop as he! How he loved himself; no peacock was more vain! And there were the jacobins and the fantails, the tumblers and the barbs, the flights, and the carriers—which weren't really carrying pigeons at all.

"What are those plain ones in the little cage? They don't look fancy like these others, but they look stronger," George said to Gramp.

"Oh, those are homers," said the old gentleman, who had been something of a pigeon expert in his day. "They are the kind that carry the messages. You take them away and tie a little message on one of their legs and let them go and they will usually find their way home."

"How do they do it?"

"I don't know, and I guess nobody does."

"Are they the only kind that can find their way home?"

"The only kind I have ever known of."

And then the two went off hand-in-hand talking about all the different kinds of pigeons, and their different behavior and appearance.

Nor did it stop there. That evening George sat on Gramp's lap while the old man recalled absorbing stories of his boyhood. To-night he told George about the many different kinds of pigeons he had kept up in the barn loft, how the hawks often got them when he let them out, and many other things that interested the boy a lot. There was something about pigeons that fascinated George more than anything had before. He could hardly stop asking questions about them when bedtime came.

Then, on his birthday somebody gave him a big book about pigeons, full of pictures and written in simple language that a nine-year-old could understand. Pigeons, pigeons, pigeons!

Pretty soon his teacher found him drawing pictures of pigeons—not at all bad drawings, either. To his parents it seemed as if George's life had suddenly come to be made up of pigeons. He spent hours before the windows of the pet shop, and presently made the acquaintance of the owner, who saw him outside the window so often that he asked him to come in and help him feed the pets.

"No," replied his little visitor, "just let me feed the pigeons." That was where he learned how and what to feed them.

If George could only have heard the discussions that took place at home on two evenings after he had gone to bed, his boyish heart would have throbbed with joy. Gramp began the first discussion by speaking to mother and Dad.

"Do you folks think George is too young to have some pigeons of his own?"

"Why," replied Dad, "surely he is. He couldn't take care of them. He would soon lose interest, just like all children, and pretty soon I'd be looking after them."

"No, you mean *I* would!" said Mother.

"Not so fast, not so fast!" Gramp went on. "I've been around with that boy lately more than either of you. We've had a lot of fun together. I don't want to go against any decision of yours, naturally, but I have a notion that some pigeons would not do him any harm. He wants some so badly—I know it—that I know he would appreciate them. If all that you are worried about is the possibility of having to take care of them, I'll tell you what I'll do: I will look after them myself, if he doesn't. And more than that, I'll guarantee to persuade him to get rid of them if he tires of them. What do you say?"

"Well, suppose you let us think it over," answered Dad. And so the subject was dropped for the time being.

But the next evening Gramp resumed it. He had set the leaven to working and he didn't mean to let it lose its effect. George had gone to bed, and once more the older people were around the lamp.

"Well, is the boy to have his pigeons?" asked Gramp.

"We haven't thought enough about it yet," answered Dad. "I am afraid that if he lets them out they will annoy the neighbors."

"Don't let them out," said Gramp.

"That would be cruel," answered Dad. "Pigeons are meant to fly."

"Not necessarily. Of course the church-steeple variety that you know are that way. But as a matter of fact many of the breeds couldn't fly far if they tried. Could you imagine a fantail pigeon flying any great distance or for a long time? No, sir. I may have brought you up in the city, where you never showed any inclination toward having pets, but that is no reason why George should feel the same. You see, he takes after me more

than you. This business of loving pets has
skipped a generation."

There were more arguments and more talking, until finally Dad was completely broken
down and could find no more replies, and then
Gramp knew he was victorious.

"Leave it to me, Paul," Gramp told him.
"You won't regret it." And Paul knew that
his father's judgment was usually good. He
himself didn't care a snap of his fingers for
pets of any kind, but he was sensible enough
to realize that if George did, he should not be
discouraged.

About ten o'clock one morning not long
afterwards, Gramp walked into the pet shop.

"Good morning, sir," he said to the owner.
"Does that little grandson of mine ever get
in your way around here? He comes so
much."

"Bless you, no. He's the best little helper
I ever had. He knows just how much to feed
every pair of pigeons in the place, and he
loves them all."

"Hmm," grunted Gramp under his breath.
"What kind of pigeons does he like best?"

"The pouters and the fantails. The homers
and the flights and the plain kinds don't interest him so much."

"Well," said Gramp, "I wish you would

help me out. I have in mind to arrange a little plot. That boy is just plain crazy about
pigeons. I want to see whether his love for
them will last. I want to get him a pair. But,
you see, I'm afraid that if I do he won't love
them so much as he would if he had bought
them himself. So here's what we will do, if
you agree. We'll make him work for a pair!
You find out which pair he likes best, and let
him think he is working for them, and I will
pay part of the cost. But I don't want him to
know a thing about it, not a thing. Is it a
go?"

The pet-shop man's face broke into a broad
smile. "That's a fine idea," he said, "but I'm
afraid the laugh is on you!" And Gramp,
much astonished, was led to the back of the
shop where the pigeons were. "See that fine-
looking pair of pouters? Well, who do you
think owns those birds, free and clear? Nobody but George! And do you see the pair of
eggs under that one? Well, that means that
George is soon going to own *four* pouter
pigeons instead of *two*. Why, that boy has
been coming here regularly and working to
pay for those birds. Last Saturday he finished paying for them, and now he is working
to buy up some food ahead. He told me that
he knew his family didn't like pets, and so he

had better tell them nothing about it. But they are his to do what he wants with."

Well—Gramp was of course pleased almost beyond words! He lost no time in getting home to talk it all over with his grandson. First he told George that his parents had consented to his having pigeons at home. Then the boy said he already had some, and Gramp admitted having learned as much from the pet-shop man, and told him to tell his parents all about it.

So—"Mother," said George, "I've worked so much for the pet-shop man that he gave me two pigeons to pay me. I just *had* to have some pigeons. Was that all right?"

"Good for you! I am glad to hear it. You certainly love those birds, don't you? Well, money that's earned spends best!"

Then every afternoon for a week, out in the back yard at 148 First Street, an old man and a boy were at work building a complete little pigeon-coop, with a door, and a nice flying cage, and some nest-boxes up in one corner of the house. But when all this was finished, then came the question of moving the birds and their eggs. George was very impatient to get them home at once, but both the pet-store man and Gramp advised him not to, so he decided to wait until the young pigeons

were hatched and could be moved with greater
safety.

It promised to be a hard wait, but luckily
Thanksgiving Day came along. George's
room was at the back of the house on the
third floor. He usually got up and dressed
about seven o'clock, but on this occasion he
was wakened a little earlier. A strange noise
seemed to echo faintly in his room. For some
minutes he listened, and then as he grew wider
awake, he recognized a sound which was to become very familiar in his life—the sound of
cooing. Quickly he jumped to the window
and peeped out. What was that in the dim
light that he saw way down below in the
cage? A pair of beautiful pigeons, as sure as
he was a foot high! He could just make out
that they were pouters, too. Never before
had he dressed so rapidly!

Down the stairs two steps at a time he flew
and out to the back yard—and there they
were. Wonderful! Was it a fairy tale?
These were blue-barred, his others were reds.
Soon he would bring his others home and then
he would have six.

Three pairs of eyes peeked out of windows
upstairs, and watched the boy jump up and
down with joy.

So George Hitchcock was now launched in

the pigeon business, all set for long, happy
years to come.

INTRODUCING RICHARD CRAMPTON

"Honestly, Richard, if I have to mend any
more holes in your trousers like these, I'll
make you go to bed early every day for a
week." His mother was working over some
large holes in Richard's trousers, while Richard himself sat watching her, with his feet
crossed and his chin resting in his hand.

"There isn't much of anything left to darn,"
she went on, "and you can't wear your best
suit. Why, I've done so much mending for
you and your brothers lately that I guess I
shall have to open a tailor shop. Thank
Heaven, your sisters don't climb fences!"

"Yes, they do," retorted Richard, "but all
they have to wear out is their bare knees, and
you don't have to mend *them*."

"Well, then, if you aren't more careful
about this fence-climbing business, you'll find
yourself dressed in girl's clothes for a while,
so I can have a rest from mending! Oh, how
I rue the day when George got those pigeons!
You boys can't do anything but look at them.
The Gardners will soon be sending your father
a bill for painting their fence, you've marked

it up so." The Misses Gardner lived in the
house just between Bud's and Dick's.

"But, Mother, I told you long ago that if
you would let me have some pigeons too, then
I wouldn't need to climb over and watch
Bud's." All the fellows called George "Bud,"
just as they called Richard "Dick."

"Well, suppose you speak to your father
to-night—maybe he won't mind. I'll tell him
I'm in favor of it, if you want them so badly."

"Oh, Mother, *will* you?" The little fellow
threw his arms about his busy mother's neck
and gave her a big squeeze.

Now, when a boy gets his mother on his
side, the rest is generally easy, and you can
readily imagine that it wasn't long before
Richard had some pigeons too. But his
weren't pouters. Not at all—his had to be
different. So he chose fantails, not extra-fine
specimens, but still, not at all bad. One was
white, one all red, and the third white and
blue. They cost him a dollar and fifty cents,
which was quite a lot of money for a ten-
year-old boy to spend.

There was now some rivalry between the
two boys, and it would be hard to say which
set of pigeons attracted more attention.
Every one who came to see Bud's always went
to see Dick's, too, and everybody who came

to see Dick's always looked at Bud's; and so
the amount of notice which they received was
about even. By winter Bud had ten pouters,
but Dick still had only three fantails.

INTRODUCING WILLIAM VAN R. BRIGHTON

His middle name was Van Rensselaer to
show that Bill was descended directly from
the old Dutch stock which first settled New
York. It was a pretty fine name and Bill was
a pretty fine boy—a husky lad with a small
mule-kick in each fist so that none of the other
boys ever dared to tease him about his aristo-
cratic middle name. Indeed, he carried the
Van Rensselaer very well.

Bill lived just around the corner from Bud
and Dick, so Bud's and Dick's back yards
backed up against his. That was why it was
so easy for Bill to look at both of their pigeon
coops whenever he wanted to. He had a little ladder which he put against the fence, and
by stepping up he could peek over and easily
see the wonderful sights. And he could also
climb over the fence, which he did quite frequently.

Bill had one brother and one sister, both
considerably older than he was, but in spite
of being the baby of the family he wasn't the
least bit spoiled. His brother had taken all of

that out of him and had thoroughly rubbed off all the corners. Everybody liked Bill.

All winter long he had looked over the back fence at the pigeons, and during the previous fall he had helped Dick make his coop.

Spring came, and now the boys got together often to watch the pigeons. This meant more fence-climbing for Dick. So one day, when he told the boys that he had to stop it because of the wear and tear on his clothes, Bill had a bright idea.

"Suppose that we get our families to let us knock off a couple of boards from our fences. If we knock off two in Dick's yard and two in Bud's, then I can go into either yard and either of you can go through my yard into the other fellow's. What do you say?"

It was decided to tackle Dick's father first. He consented at once when Mother told him about the mending. The next step was to secure the permission of Bill's father. Of course he had to say yes because Dick's father had; if he said no, it would not appear very neighborly. Then it was easy to get Bud's father to fall in with the plan by telling him that the others had agreed.

Spring had come. The grass was green, trees were budding, and the pigeons were cooing louder than ever before. The first thing the boys knew, two pairs of Bud's pouters were sitting on eggs. But those fantails! There was something wrong with them. All they did was fight. After some time Gramp was called into consultation with the three boys.

"Looks to me as if they were all of the same sex—probably all males—cock birds. Get some hen pigeons and maybe you will have better luck." This had never occurred to the boys. But they took his advice and all three decided that it would be best to take one to the pet store and trade it for another, and then buy a second hen pigeon, to make two pairs.

So Dick traded the white one first, because he had the fewest feathers in his tail and didn't hold his head back so far as the other two. They turned in the pigeon and twenty-five cents, and got a fine-looking white hen instead. Then for the new one they bought a very beautiful silver hen—a stylish little bird, who was vain because she was so good-looking.

Oh, what good times Dick and Bud were having! Bill had been sharing in them, of course, but he was still an outsider. Now nothing else would do but that he, too, must have some pigeons.

What kind would he buy? Could he get his parents to allow him to have some? These were very big questions, but eventually they were settled. No indoor pigeons for Bill! His were going to be the kind that would fly, the kind he could let out, but they would have to be fancy ones. So Bill decided on tumblers.

His pigeon house was not going to be any little affair either. His father was a contractor, and Bill was very handy with tools himself. So one day the three boys went down to Bill's father's great supply yard to look over some old lumber. As they were searching, what should their curious eyes discover but a little tool house, all in pieces, and just about large enough for a perfect pigeon house. Bill ran to the office. "Dad, may I have that little tool house that is all knocked down in sections? It's just what I need." His father walked out and looked at it carefully.

"Yes," he said, "but it needs new roofing paper, and the glass must be put in the window. If you will repair it yourself and put it in first-class shape, you may have it." The very next day, it was delivered by one of Mr. Brighton's trucks right to the house and the men carried it through the house and stood it up against the fence in the back yard.

That afternoon the fun began. Three husky boys went to work, with plenty of will but with little experience. Gramp helped them to get the house together and showed them just how to make it fit as it should. By night it was done—but not without much hammering, several pounded fingers, and a black-and-blue spot where the roof had fallen on Dick's foot when they were trying to raise it. However, even black-and-blue spots have a way of clearing up, and pretty soon you can't even tell where they were.

The house had been set in a corner of Bill's back yard. Now began the task of making a little fly for the pigeons. Some wire was obtained from the store, some staples, and a few two-by-four sticks of wood. The fence supplied the back of the fly, and the house supplied one side; so all that had to be built was the front, one side, the top, and a door. The boys did it all without assistance.

The day after it was finished, Miss Mary Gardner, who with her sister had been taking a great interest in the proceedings, stepped into the Brightons' yard to see Bill. He was her favorite of the three boys. Bill was very fond of her too. She had heard that Bill wanted some pigeons, but she didn't know about his ambition to own a pair of tumblers. All she said was, "Bill, you leave it to me. I'll get you some pigeons that will make every boy in the neighborhood wish he were you." So Bill left it to Miss Mary, but not without some grave misgivings.

On her way down town Miss Mary stopped at a fine pet shop and ordered some pigeons.

"I want to buy some pigeons for a young friend," she said to the pet-shop man. "Six of the best-looking ones you have, and I'm going to pick them out—six different kinds so he can have variety."

What a funny order! The pet-shop man, who was an Italian, tried in his broken English to explain that she ought to buy pairs, but Miss Mary didn't understand him very well, and anyway she had her mind made up.

So, after looking around, she picked out six that took her eye. "Send them to 762 Douglas Avenue. How much will they be?"

"Four dollars and a half." Miss Mary paid and took her departure.

Was Bill a very happy boy, or not, when he looked inside of the box that had been delivered to his home while he was away at school? Perhaps, if he had not learned so much about pigeons from Bud's and Dick's, he would have been. Instead, when he looked inside he was terribly upset. To think of such ignorance! How could anybody spend so much money and be so stupid?

"Why," he stormed, "there is not a single *pair* of pigeons in the box. They are everything. Mother, what shall I do with them? I s'pose I have got to keep them, just because Miss Mary gave them to me. What would she say if she found I had sold them or traded them? Darn it! I'm not even going to thank her for them. How could she be so stupid?"

"Bless your heart, sonny, I wouldn't let that bother me," said his mother. "Go and let them out in the pen you have made, and watch them for a while. Go and get the other boys, and maybe you will find that you like some one of these better than the tumblers you wanted so badly. Cheer up! Here's a quarter—take it and buy some pigeon feed. I know just how you feel. After all the trouble that people have taken in the past to make these breeds as pure as they are, it certainly would be a shame to mix them up. Each bird must have a mate of its own kind; you are right. But don't worry. If you want to change them, I'll make it all right with Miss Mary."

And then Bill felt better. He had a quarter, and six pigeons, and his mother's promise. His tears dried, and soon the sun began to break through the clouds again.

Now there was nothing to do but run for the other boys. So he ran to Bud's yard and, poking his head through the fence, whistled the whistle that was their private call. Then without waiting for Bud to answer he went to the hole in Dick's fence and whistled for Dick. Soon both boys came running.

And so all three boys were now launched in the pigeon business.

Chapter III

PIGEON SHOWS

THE pigeons were turned loose in the new coop at the rear of the yard. As things now stood there were six pigeons and three boys, with a big problem to be solved. Bill got over his impatience at Miss Mary's ignorance, and remembered that she really meant to please him, and that she had never kept pigeons herself and so had never thought of keeping the breeds pure. But, as he said to Bud and Dick, "Now suppose that we mate that great big red Carneaux, which is twice as big as any of the others, with that little turbit—what good would the squabs be? They would be mongrels. And if we mated that tumbler with that barb, I'll bet the squabs wouldn't turn out to be good for anything. That's the trouble. I don't believe in mixing breeds."

"Well, what are you going to do?" asked Dick.

"I've got it!" said Bud. "Let's have a pigeon show, just like a poultry show, and charge admission. Then we can whack up on the money we take in and buy some more pigeons."

"Not a bad idea. But where can we hold it?" questioned Dick.

"Oh, right out in the back yard. We can make some signs and put one up over each bird and let Gramp be the judge," answered Bud.

Saturday came, a bright, sunny day. The show opened at ten. But before that time the birds were taken from their coops and put into improvised cages made of old orange and grapefruit boxes. Where there were pairs, they were put in the cages together, but each of Bill's had to have a separate cage for itself. Gramp came, and with great judicial dignity decided on the best among the fantails and the pouters; but when he came to judge Bill's, they were all different, so he gave the prize to the tumbler as being the best of the six that Bill had. In all, forty-five children paid a dime each to see the show, and it was a great success.

And now Bill could go about getting the tumblers which he had wanted for so long. Putting the six birds into a box with some holes in the top, off the three boys started to do a little trading. After visiting two pet shops, they returned with six new tumblers, three pairs already mated. All of the old ones were gone. Miss Mary was invited out to see them, because Bill's mother had had a little talk with her and everything had been arranged to the satisfaction of all concerned.

On Gramp's advice, Bill let his new charges all get very well acquainted with their home and finish building their nests before he let them out for the first time. And when he did, they did very little flying, nor did he lose one. First he let out two, not both of the same pair. When these had come back to their mates and had learned the way to get inside the coop after several days' trials, then he liberated two more. Thus all of them were soon acquainted with the coop.

After a week, all six were flying together. They would circle around and then one would give a quick flip and turn a somersault in the air. One of them always turned three times, seldom more or less. But one was Bill's best bird. He was a roller. When he tumbled he would keep it up until it seemed that he would strike a roof or drop right down to the ground. And yet he never seemed to hit anything. Sometimes he would roll down for a great distance. How the boys loved to watch him!

The fantails and pouters were all right, but somehow the fine tumblers were such clever fliers that they captured the boys' hearts. Had it not been for a suggestion from Gramp, I'm afraid all of them would have traded their birds for tumblers.

Fall was coming, and each of the boys had so increased the numbers of his pigeons that

POUTER   FAN TAIL   TUMBLER

it was beginning to look as if the coops would have to be enlarged, or else some birds be disposed of. Even though the rats had killed a few of each boy's pigeons, and the cats had killed two of Bill's young tumblers, nevertheless the pigeons had increased.

"Boys," said Gramp one day, "why don't you enter your pigeons in the Madison Square Garden Poultry Show? I think you have some birds good enough to get some prizes."

That sounded like a good idea, but the boys were young and, while they had heard of this wonderful show, they had never thought of their pigeons getting prizes. But when Gramp promised to take care of entering their birds for them, they quickly agreed.

Each boy entered his four best birds. It was indeed a great occasion. There isn't any "garden" at Madison Square now, but when the boys exhibited their pigeons for the first time, it was in the historic old Garden that they showed them.

They made an early start with Gramp, each boy carrying his own. They reached the entrance and showed their tickets. Down the long entry-way they went, and even before they had reached the inside door they could hear the crowing of roosters, the cackling of hens, and a general bedlam.

They had to go up the stairs to reach the pigeon cages on the balcony. There they could look down on the myriads of cages of chickens of every description, and of ducks and geese; and there too were large cages with beautiful waterfowl and the rare birds that are used to decorate fine estates. On their way they passed the cages of guinea-pigs and rabbits, and these, too, interested them.

Finally they came to the pigeon section, and

then they looked for their numbers. Here were a lot of fantails. Oh, yes, here was one of Dick's numbers. So he took the right bird out and put him in the cage. Then he quickly found the others and soon had them all placed. In the same way the other boys found the proper places for their pigeons.

"Looks to me as if you boys had some birds quite as good as any I have seen," said Gramp. They had brought their lunch, so they stayed and watched the proceedings.

As soon as all of the exhibits were placed, and ten o'clock had come, the aisles were roped off and the judges went to work.

During the judging, the boys walked around looking at everything, even the cages of mice and rats with their many colors. The geese and turkeys pleased them immensely, and the waterfowl in the big cage gave them much to think about.

When the judging of the pigeons was nearly over they spent an hour inspecting the different kinds. For some time they watched the tricks of the parlor tumblers which couldn't fly at all. Some of the fanciers of these birds brought them out in a wide aisle and, as the judges looked on, they let them go. They would roll down the aisle twenty feet or so, just as Bill's did in the air. Others jumped

up, made only one turn, and landed squarely
on their feet; while still others made more
than one turn. Great sport! A wonderful
time they were having!

But what interested them more than anything else was the homers. In one group were
fifty or more, all of whom were called five-
hundred-mile birds.

"What does that mean, Gramp—five-hun-
dred-mile birds?" asked Bud.

"Why, they are pigeons that have been
taken five hundred miles away, and have been
liberated, and have returned home. Usually
they will fly that far within a day. Really,
that is the best sport one can have with
pigeons. When you boys get a little older, I
believe you will want to have homers rather
than any other kind."

Get a little older? Why no, that would
never do—they began right that very minute
to want some. But each was loyal to his own
kind, which he liked to feel was just about the
best thing in pigeons. However, they could
not get that idea of homers out of their minds.
Maybe they could have some too.

They looked around and here were more
homers. None of them were showy; all of
them looked like business and they were of
many colors. In fact, the color seemed to

have nothing to do with their ability as fliers, judging from the appearance of the birds at the show. There was something about the homers that made the boys' imaginations work. The idea that you could take one of those little birds far away from home, and that it would find its way back! That was wonderful.

By evening the judging was finished and the boys were more than ready to go home. They were so tired from all the walking and standing that their legs ached.

There was one thing they could never forget: that they had won some prizes. Dick's fantails had captured a second and a third. Bud's pouters had won a third, and Bill's tumblers had won two thirds. And who could say that was not very fine for three boys who had never owned a pigeon before that year and who had never before attended a poultry show in their lives? Now they had something bigger to work for. None of them was content to take a third. Next year they would win higher honors. And now they had before them a whole year to get hold of some better stock and to breed some better birds.

"I believe," said Gramp, "that you have done the best you can with what you have. You can't get blood out of a turnip, or, as it says in the Bible, 'Men do not gather grapes from thorns nor figs from thistles.' You will have to get hold of some better stock from some one who has the best." Good advice, Gramp! The boys knew it was. The only trouble was, they were now too ambitious. They wanted to start at the top right away.

During the next few weeks all three sent out letters in their boyish handwriting to the men who owned the best stock. The Madison Square Garden Poultry Show catalogue was well thumbed-up as they read with difficulty the names of the breeds and the men who had won. Generally the replies which they received took not a little ambition out of them. The prices for the stock were beyond reach. Christmas had passed, so there was no hope of their parents' giving them pigeons for presents. Now it became a matter of working for the money, of trading pigeons, of selling them—anything to get enough to buy even a pair of the very best. One of their most profitable methods was to call on all of their friends and relatives and collect old newspapers, which they then kept until they had several hundred pounds, and these they sold to the paper-dealer. Every hundred pounds brought them in forty cents. During the winter they had hauled many hundred pounds on their sleds and on a little wagon. And by the time spring came each boy had saved eight dollars; that is, they had collected twenty-four dollars among them, and it was divided into thirds. Shoveling snow had also helped. Always the boys worked together.

Finally, after much letter-writing, each succeeded in buying a pair of pigeons of his chosen variety. Dick had his sent from out West, but Bud and Bill found theirs in New York, and on several Saturdays they went with Gramp to inspect or buy them. By May each boy owned pigeons that he hoped would produce prize-winners, or win prizes themselves.

Chapter IV

SUCCESS

THREE years passed, and the friendship of the three boys had strengthened steadily. Their pigeons had grown in numbers and in quality. All of the boys had been sick at one time or another. Once Bud and Dick had had scarlet fever, and Bill had to look after their pigeons for them. Once Bill had had tonsilitis, which kept him in bed for two weeks, and his chores fell upon the other boys, but there was no complaint. They had grown in the three years, too, and were nearly as tall as their parents.

Meanwhile the boys had taken more and more interest in the pigeons and the shows. The second year had not been so profitable as they had hoped, but they won some prizes and on the whole built up increasingly better flocks. But the third year found their birds greatly improved, and indeed very little of the old stock with which they had started was left to them, so much trading had they done. Somehow there was not much about any one

pigeon to inspire especial affection and loy-
alty. The pouters pouted and strutted about,
the fantails vainly coquetted, and the tumblers tumbled, but none of these by any of its
charms could win a place in the hearts of the
boys. It was easy for them to sell or trade
any bird. Their one common interest lay in
constantly improving, improving, improving.
The whole breed was the love of each boy,
not any particular pigeon. Had it not been
for this steady ambition to improve the breed
by continually mating the best, it is quite
likely that the boys would long ago have lost
interest.

By the third year they were at the top, having won the majority of first prizes in the
classes in which they had entered their birds.
To cap the climax they had won the most
coveted honors at Madison Square Garden.
With these victories won, all that was left to
them was the further improvement of their
breeds. Each boy took almost as much interest in his friends' pigeons as he did in his own,
and this made their partnership all the firmer.

Quite often they received very flattering
offers for their best birds, but they always refused. Indeed one of the advantages of the
pigeon business was that, because the boys
had the best, the birds paid their own way.

That is, the boys could sell enough stock so that they needed to spend very little of their own allowances. Altogether the pigeons ate a surprising amount, but the cost of this did not equal what the boys took in from their sales. And this pleased their parents—the experience was making them into young business men, and they were coming to understand the real value of money.

During these years with the growth of the boys' interest their flocks had gradually increased. Larger quarters had been needed, so more commodious coops had been built. The boys built them together. As they became more and more proficient in carpentry, the new coops reflected better workmanship than the earlier ones. Bill's had not needed enlarging, but the fly was lengthened by extending it across the entire width of the back yard.

One summer Bud went to a boys' camp, and during that time the other boys faithfully cared for his pigeons. The following summer Dick went to the country with his family, and it was his birds this time that had to be taken care of.

Nor should we forget the Misses Gardner, who were really most excellent friends of the boys and the finest kind of neighbors. They took great interest in the boys' activities and

frequently invited them in for fresh dough-
nuts and cocoa. They occasionally passed
nice pieces of cake or slices of pie over the
fence to them, and in every way encouraged
them, finally suggesting that they knock some
boards off their fences on both sides so that it
would be easier for the boys to go back and
forth—which was very convenient.

Chapter V

FANCY PIGEONS ARE FINE, BUT—

THREE fourteen-year-old boys sat in Bill Brighton's room on the top floor of his house, a snug little room with pictures of pigeons in evidence, and several silver cups on the mantelpiece. Banners of high schools and colleges added touches of color. A large blue banner marked "Yale" in white letters a foot high across the wall above the mantel indicated the college of Bill's choice. Both Bill's and Bud's fathers were Yale graduates.

The boys were sitting around a card-table, each with a book recording the hatching dates —birthdays—of their pigeons, and what had happened to each during the past year. Many slips of paper with scribbling on them formed the basis for their records. For a long while they worked in silence.

"Fellows," Dick said suddenly, "would you think I was yellow if I tell you what's been on my mind for a long while? I hate to be a quitter, but I must get it out."

43

"What's the matter? What is it, Dick?" they asked him.

"Promise you won't think I am yellow if I tell you?"

"Sure. We know you too well for that," answered Bill. "What's on your mind?"

"Well, I'll tell you," said Dick. "You know these fantails of mine are lots of fun, but for the last week I've been carrying this clipping around in my pocket and, to tell you the truth, it has set me thinking." He unfolded a well-worn newspaper clipping.

"Listen to what it says: 'Ross's birds win Pigeon Futurity. Three birds home before another is clocked in great 100-mile race.' And it tells all about the rest of the homers, too. Do you know, fellows, I just can't get that out of my mind. And then again I keep thinking about something else too. Do you remember how we all liked those homers the first time we put our birds in the Garden show? Do you remember how Gramp told us that some day we would be old enough to have some birds like those? Well, I have never forgotten a word he said, and although I've been having a wonderful time with my fantails, still I have always had a feeling that I would like to own some great homers."

Yellow? No, he wasn't. Both boys soon

showed him that instead of being yellow he was really brave, for he had had the courage to say just what each of them had been thinking for a long while. Both quickly told Dick how they felt, and it was no time at all before they had decided that they were going to sell their birds and buy homers. It was a big decision, made by three determined boys.

This provided them with something new to think about, something different to plan for, and thus added a new interest to their lives. No longer would they breed pigeons that were more ornamental than useful; now they would be in the ranks of those who took great risks and very often stood to lose. Now they would be dependent on forces beyond their control— they would have wind, storms, hawks and other difficulties to cope with. But they felt that the reward would be worth the risk.

It was settled then and there that while they were disposing of their old pigeons, they would take plenty of time to study the best methods of housing, raising and flying homing pigeons together with all the details that might contribute to the success of the venture.

The first step was to make inquiries of a number of homing-pigeon fanciers. They found many listed in the show catalogue, and from the Homing Pigeon Club they obtained the names of others. They spent as many evenings and Saturday afternoons as they could, visiting these men. Most of them were very cordial, and the boys learned a great deal, especially about house design, and all of the specifications, even to the trap, that ingenious little arrangement of wires through which the pigeons can push to get into the house, but out of which they cannot go. They learned what materials made the most satisfactory nest-boxes, the best perches and nest-bowls, and found that much of the equipment already on hand would do very well.

All of their spare time during the winter was spent in this study and in disposing of their pouters, fantails and tumblers. By March all the fancy birds were gone, and now came the task of securing the homing-pigeon stock, and building the accommodations.

"George," called a cheerful voice from the Gardners' kitchen window, "will you come here a minute?"

"Be right over," replied the boy, who had just been standing in the snow looking at his empty pigeon-coop. In a few jumps he had come through the fence and in a few more had entered the door to face Miss Mary.

"George, I've been almost sick thinking about your pigeons. What's the matter?

Have you given them up?   Did some one complain of the cooing?   I have wondered and wondered what you are going to do.   Please excuse my curiosity, but tell me, son, what it is all about!"

"Oh, thank you, Miss Mary," said Bud, "but the truth is we have got rid of our pigeons only for a time.   We've each wanted to have another kind of pigeons—homers. That's why we've been selling our others and studying about the new kind.   When it is warmer we're going to build a great big house and have plenty of room for them to fly, and keep all of our pigeons together.   There won't be three separate coops any longer but just one extra-big one, where we can keep a hundred or two hundred pigeons if we want to."

"Oh, won't that be wonderful?" said Miss Gardner, almost as enthusiastic over the prospect as the boy was.   "Go on, tell me some more."

"The main coop or house is going to be in both Bill's yard and mine, half and half. Then we're going to move the little house, the one now in Bill's yard, over into Dick's, and we will keep there any birds that are sick or should not be with the others.   Then we have decided also to have a fly on the other side of the house in Bill's yard, but there'll be very little room in my yard, for the house will about fill the space."

"Why, what ambitious plans you have! I only wish I were a boy and could be doing all this planning and everything with you. It must be great fun."

"You bet it is," answered Bud, "but that isn't all. We are going to make divisions inside, and the little room that will be occupied by our racing birds is going to be finished off like a ballroom for pigeons. Wait till you see it. It's going to be so nice that you will want to stay there instead of in your own house!"

"Yes, your plans do sound interesting. But tell me, George, are you going to have enough exercising space for the birds that are not racers? I should think there would scarcely be sufficient room."

"You're right, Miss Mary. That is our greatest problem. Our parents won't let us run the house or a fly back more than eight feet into our yards on account of the flowers and the room needed to dry clothes. We won't have very much space for a flying cage."

"Ethel," called Miss Mary to her sister, "won't you come here?" Her sister joined them.

"Now, George, tell my sister just what you have told me. I'm sure she is quite as much interested as I am." So Bud repeated the plans and even added a few details that he had left out in the first telling.

"Ethel," said Miss Mary, "I have an idea for your approval. Let us talk it over, George. You run over home and come back in just fifteen minutes."

So George went home and wondered all through that fifteen minutes what the two sisters had in mind. It was a long wait, but he was back again on time.

"Now, George, here's what we can contribute to your pigeon-coop plans. We suggest that you build your flying cage across the back of *our* yard. Then we can watch the pigeons and enjoy them and you can have the additional room that you need."

"Oh, no—Miss Mary—Miss Ethel—you can't mean it! Wait till I tell the fellows. They will be crazy over it! Thanks, a lot! I'll be back soon, but I can't wait to tell them." And Bud hustled out of the door and off to tell the other boys.

Needless to say, they were both as happy as Bud. Now the only real obstacle to their plans was overcome, and they could build their pigeon house, and a real one it would be.

"Say, fellows, this house will be as big as a city. It will be a pigeon city for sure," said Bill one day.

"That's an idea. That's what we'll call it," said Dick, *"Pigeon City.* It will be a city for pigeons, all right. But there is one way it will differ from most cities. This is going to be a snobbish city, exclusive, nothing like New York. There will be only one breed allowed. Nor will there be any slums within its borders, because we won't have any of the kind of pigeons that make pigeon slums."

"Only one breed—homers," Bill and Bud echoed.

"Yes, homers," said Dick, "but remember there are homers *and* homers, and Pigeon City will be a city for only the very best homers."

Chapter VI

PIGEON CITY IS BEGUN

By using their patent formula of persuading one boy's father to say yes, then going to the second and obtaining his permission, and with the consent of the two going to the third —who then couldn't possibly refuse—all plans were approved.

But better than that, one day the fathers of the three boys, together with Gramp, held a consultation in the interest of their children.

"Gentlemen," said Gramp to them, "I seriously doubt whether there are three boys anywhere who know more about pigeons than our boys do. I know a little myself, but the boys beat me. Why, if you could see the libraries they have on the subject, if you could see the respect in which they are held by old pigeon-breeders, if you could see how earnestly they have tackled their job of breeding the best possible, then you would do all you can to help them. Surely they are worthy of it."

The three fathers needed no convincing. They had seen with their own eyes, they had

heard with their own ears, and they were as
eager to help as was Gramp to have them. So
when Mr. Brighton agreed to supply the boys
with second-hand lumber from his yards, each
of the fathers agreed to contribute money for
the wire and the roofing paper. Then they
told the boys what they had decided, and all
three were overjoyed. By this time the boys
were very clever in the use of tools, and so,
with the help of Gramp, the house would be
good-looking.

It was now the middle of March. A truck
backed up to the Brightons' house and for half
an hour men carried boards, rafters, and stud-
ding out to the back yard. The next day the
hardware truck arrived at the Hitchcocks',
and several rolls of chicken wire of an extra
heavy grade were delivered into the back
yard. That same afternoon another truck delivered to the Cramptons' yard two large rolls
of fine-quality roofing paper, boxes containing
nails, and staples for the wire. So now all was
ready for the boys to go ahead.

During the first part of the month the old
houses and the wire flying-cages had all been
taken down. The house in Bill's yard had
been transferred to Dick's, and this time set
up on stilts three feet high. It was at the right
side of the yard, because the plans called for

a great fly to be erected to reach across both the Gardner and Crampton yards. Then the pigeons would be able to fly over and sit on the top of the house in Dick's yard where they could sun themselves.

First the stilts for the house were set into the ground. Then a platform was built across the top of them, and two pairs of steps were made, one in Bill's yard, and one in Bud's. The floor was just sixteen feet square and the fence divided it, but the fence now stood only four feet up above the floor.

No sooner was the floor finished than the uprights were set in place, just as a contractor builds the structure of a frame house. This was not a very great task, and it was completed in two afternoons. After the windows had been set in place the side boards were put on, and the next job was the roof. This was peaked, with only a gradual slope. At the end of two weeks the roofing paper had been put on, the doors fitted with hinges, and the paint applied; and they were ready to tackle the interior.

Before they started this, however, they made a very wise decision. Their new idea came from Gramp, who had never ceased to take an interest in their affairs and had given them many a good suggestion.

"While you are waiting for your house to be completed, why not put some birds to work raising squabs in the little house in Dick's yard?"

"Great! That's a fine idea," said Bill. "We can save at least a month because the pigeons are all nesting and laying. It's the best time of the year."

Now, if they hadn't had so much experience, the boys might have gone about their new plan unwisely, but by this time they knew exactly what to do. First, they finished quickly the big fly between the main house and Dick's so that the birds could be raising squabs while the boys were completing the interior of the main house. The fly rose above the fencetops over four feet, giving the pigeons plenty of room to exercise in. The hammering in the main house would not make enough noise to disturb them.

The fly completed, the boys did not buy a single homing pigeon. Instead they went to the meat market. Every week-end the wholesale market received a shipment of pigeons. The boys could now tell the cocks from the hens by looking at them, and so they bought six pairs of pigeons from the butcher, making sure all of them were husky-looking and old enough to breed.

These were taken home and thus were saved for a few months from being eaten. They were turned loose in the great fly where they enjoyed themselves. Then two pairs at a time were mated. Now mating a pair of pigeons is not hard, and once mated they will stay mated for the rest of their lives. The boys had special little mating cages. They were divided through the middle by partitions which could be easily taken out. One of a pair was put into one side; the other into the other. After a short time the old cock pigeon would begin to strut in front of his prospective mate. He would coo and rush forward, dragging his tail spread out wide. Then the hen pigeon would make eyes at him, so to speak, and if she liked him would sidle up to the partition. When the boys were sure that the pigeons were pretty well acquainted, they would remove the partition and the two birds would coo and bill, which is the way pigeons kiss. Then they were pronounced married, and let out to fly around the flying cage. Soon they would be making a nest and the hen would be laying eggs. That was the process of mating the several pairs of pigeons. In ten days it was all over.

The nest-boxes in the house were not like those to be installed in the new house. But

they served very well. Each had an earthen-
ware nest-bowl in it. In a few days the birds
were building nests, and before long the boys
knew they would be laying a pair of eggs
apiece, allowing a day between eggs. So now
the boys began contracting for homing pigeons
in a form which you would scarcely recognize
as pigeons, namely, eggs. They had made the
acquaintance of several of the men who owned
the very best homing pigeons in and around
New York City. Furthermore, Dick had a
cousin in the army who was stationed in the
same building in which lived the officer in
charge of the United States Government
homing pigeons. The officer's name was Captain Grant. This cousin told him about Dick
and his friends and their plans to go into the
homing-pigeon game. Whereupon the army
officer, remembering his own boyhood days
and his happiness with homing pigeons,
offered to start the boys out right.

The time had now come to visit the Government pigeon loft and to make the acquaintance of Captain Grant. When their pigeons
had all made nests and each had a pair of
eggs, the boys telephoned Dick's cousin, who
made an appointment for them, and they came
on Saturday carrying a little box filled with
cotton.

They told Captain Grant in detail about their plans and why they wanted eggs. "If you will sell us some eggs, we will carry them home very carefully and put them under our pigeons, which are all ready for them. We shall have no trouble raising good pigeons, and when they have served their purpose we shall get rid of the mongrels; they are only meat pigeons. Maybe we shall have each pair raise three sets of squabs, but they will give us a great start."

"Easy enough," said the Captain. "I will let you have four pairs of eggs to carry home. And, boys," he said emphatically, "take care of them, for there is no better stock of homing pigeons in the world. These are the very choicest that it has been possible to develop. They have been raised from birds that have had to prove their ability every generation. Not one of their ancestors for many generations has failed to return from at least five hundred miles in a day. So how could they help being wonderful?"

He climbed up and took from the finest birds he had sitting at the time four pairs of eggs, marking each with a pencil so that the boys could identify them. Then, after a few instructions, he bade them good luck and promised to help them all he could. After expressing their profound appreciation they left for home. Nobody ever carried a box of anything so gingerly as the boys carried that box of eggs in their cotton nests. Upon their arrival they at once took the eggs out from under the meat pigeons and destroyed them. In place of them they substituted those from the great racing homers. The meat pigeons never knew the difference.

On the following Monday evening they went to see Mr. Ross, a breeder of renown. From him they bought two more pairs of eggs, and put these under the other meat pigeons. Now they could go to work on the interior of their main house and let the pigeons hatch out birds to which they were absolutely no relation, birds of a much higher grade than their "parents."

Chapter VII

PIGEON CITY IS COMPLETED

THE boys and the pigeons worked diligently. In due time both brought forth their finished products. There were ten healthy young pigeons as a result of the twelve eggs which had been placed under the meat pigeons —the nurses. As soon as they were old enough to leave the parents, and the parents had gone about making other nests and had laid eggs, more high-grade homing-pigeon eggs were slipped under them and their own thrown away. Again this was repeated, and after the third lot had been raised, the proprietors of Pigeon City had twenty-eight of the finest homing pigeons in the country. None but the best for Pigeon City! That was their motto, and the boys meant to live up to it.

As to Pigeon City itself, there were four rooms. One was reserved for a grain room, where the feed was stored, and there was a shelf that contained a bottle of disinfectant and a few medicines. In here were mating cages. A second room was reserved for the

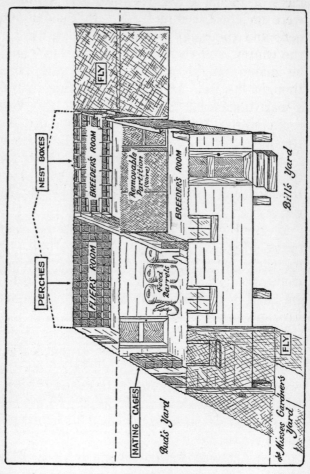

Pigeon City had four rooms

fliers or racing birds. A third and a fourth were for the breeding birds. In the fall the hens and the cocks were to be separated for the winter, and then in the spring they could be mated up to new partners if the boys thought it wise. During the breeding season a partition was removed between the two rooms so that the old birds could have greater freedom. These two rooms were both lined on two sides with nest-boxes, giving plenty of space to raise all the birds necessary to replace those that might be lost in training or in the races.

As the boys had promised, the racers' compartment was really the finest room of all. It was lined with thin boards, and the perches were arranged along three sides of the walls. In all it was large enough to accommodate fifty or more pigeons. Up in the ceiling was the trap through which the birds entered from the outside. This was arranged so that a slide could be closed over the hole to prevent the warm air from going out in the winter. The whole house was carefully sheathed to make it as warm as possible, although pigeons can stand great cold.

Pigeon racing for the young birds usually starts in the fall. All spring and summer the birds are raised to be ready for the races. So

the boys were very ambitious to have as many
birds as possible ready for the training flies
and the big flies. Therefore they considered
themselves fortunate to have as many as
twenty-eight powerful pigeons. Each had a
little solid aluminum band put on its leg in
the first few days of life, when the toes were
very pliable and soft. As the leg and toes
grew, it was impossible to remove the band
without cutting. These bands had been obtained from the great central organization of
homing-pigeon clubs, which numbered and
distributed them, allowing a certain quota to
each fancier who bought them.

As soon as Pigeon City was completed, the
boys issued a few invitations to their parents
and friends, and an inspection and jubilee took
place. Everybody was pleasantly surprised
and complimented the boys highly. The
parents were proud indeed of their sons' ac-
complishments, and the friends were happy
to know about what they had been doing.

About that time the first pigeons were
ready. When they were six weeks old they
were transferred to the room for the fliers.
This was a memorable occasion. The ten
seemed to feel at home from the first. They
ate and drank, and flew from perch to perch,

and out of the window into the fly on the other side of the great loft.

One day, after they had become thoroughly accustomed to their new compartment, they were allowed to discover that the trap was open and that they could go unhampered into the outer world. As soon as one had gone out the others followed. How they did flap their wings! One big, powerful-looking red-checked bird stood on tiptoe and flapped his wings so hard that soon he was twenty feet up in the air. The others flew up lesser distances and then came down. Then, as though frightened, they flew up at the slightest disturbance, or even when one would suddenly flap his wings. After an hour of this and of sitting in the sun, or walking along the top of the wire flying cages looking inside at the birds that had hatched and raised them, they suddenly all began to try their wings a little more. In a flock they flew up, up, up, in a few wild circles, and again they settled down. Then one of the boys whistled a call which they had come to associate with feeding-time, so at once they began to look for the way to get in. The wires of the trap were of course left wide open as they had been when the birds had gone out, so they had little trouble in getting back into the loft, much to the satisfaction and relief of all three of their owners.

Then, day after day they were allowed their freedom, until they were so much accustomed to returning through the entrance after their flies of inspection about the neighborhood, that the boys felt safe in letting down the wires of the trap and allowing them to learn how to push their way through them. After that it was a simple matter each morning to liberate the flock before going to school. If the homers felt like it they might fly for half an hour at a time for the pure joy of it. Or if so inclined, they sometimes stayed in the air only a minute or so. Thus the boys could go to school and know that when they returned they would find their pigeons safe inside.

When the next lot came along, they were added to the first, and that helped to train them; likewise for the third. And now all twenty-eight were in one comely flock.

Oh, what joy it was to see them circle in beautiful flight far up above the housetops, soar in great circles, and sometimes go off for half an hour, perhaps to return from a direction opposite to that in which they had gone! How many miles could they travel in that time? How much country could they

Oh, what joy it was to see them circle in flight far
above the housetops!

learn to recognize? How many landmarks could they isolate so that they might know them again when they returned from great distances? No one knows; but needless to say, with their eagle eyes, very little escaped them.

Nor was it only the boys who enjoyed them. Most of the neighbors also took pride in Pigeon City. The Misses Gardner especially delighted in watching the birds almost as much as the boys, and frequently came out and stood with them in the afternoon to see the pigeons perform.

There was no longer any more use for the old meat pigeons and they were taken back to the wholesaler and resold to him. It was not without a little grief, however, that the boys parted with these birds which had been so faithful in raising the finer pigeons for them. But they knew there was danger in having such birds, because if they were to mate with the finer stock, they would produce young that would be of no value as fliers, and all the careful selection of generations would have gone for naught. No, there was no use taking chances: the nursemaids must go. Pigeon City was exclusive. None but the best could live there!

Now for the inventory. July was here.

The birds were all moved into their new house.
The boys had twenty-eight pigeons, and they
knew that they had the very best of the best.
Now, how could they train them carefully so
as to eliminate the danger of losing many of
them? For they wanted to have as many as
possible to start the next year as breeders,

but by the traditions of the best fanciers,
every bird must prove its mettle. Every one
during its first year must fly one hundred and
fifty miles, or it will not be used as a breeder,
because such a bird would never come home;
but more than that, it must come home within
a day. So the standard was set high indeed.

Already there were a few birds which took
the eyes of the boys. These homers had a
magnetism which won a fellow over. Each
boy had his favorites, but none would admit it

until after the first training was over, and then the attachments began to form. They found out soon enough that the homers were different in many ways from the fantails, the pouters and the tumblers. No longer was it a case of "improve the flock." Now each boy began to love one bird, or perhaps two. The whole flock was dear to them, but each had favorites which he hoped would be among the great fliers that were sure to develop.

Chapter VIII

TRAINING PIGEON CITY'S FLIERS

ALTHOUGH the boys could hardly wait until it was time to train their birds, they had misgivings. Suppose the pigeons should not return! After all their pains and plans! So naturally, although they were glad to start out with their boxes of homing pigeons, they were fearful of results. They decided that the first fly would be from a very short distance, because the birds had not yet developed the confidence they would later. So they carried the birds to a park not over a mile away, and when they had mounted a hill they opened the boxes. The birds rose in a flock and circled higher and higher, far up into the sky. The boys noticed that the circles grew ever wider, and yet the birds seemed to move slowly in the direction of home. When they could no longer see the flock the boys ran all the way home and scrambled into the loft. But lo, not a pigeon was to be seen. Oh, what a feeling of emptiness! Not a bird home in that short fly!

"But wait—let's look outside, boys," said Bill.

And they went outside and looked. Far up in the blue they saw a flock of pigeons flying, just as their flock had so often flown. For many minutes the flock continued flying in circles. Finally some impulse seemed to direct it to descend lower and lower until soon the birds were all on the roof of Pigeon City. As they approached, the boys went into the loft, and when Bud whistled, all twenty-eight birds came rushing in for food and water, all except one red-checked bird, the largest of the lot, which slowly straggled in when he got good and ready.

A few minutes passed. "I hear another on the roof," said Dick. "Can't you hear him walking around?" Yes, sure enough they could. So the boys counted and found that their twenty-eight birds were all home.

"It must be a stray," said Bill. Then, peeking outside, he found that the birds had brought home a stranger pigeon of another breed. And in due time he found his way into the trap.

"That was a profitable training fly," they agreed, for they took the new arrival to the pet shop and sold it. But it was only the first of many such experiences, all of which added to their income. Once in a while strangers had dropped in with Bill's tumblers, but not very frequently. Now with the training and the circling, the homers brought many stray birds back with them.

The next training fly was at a greater distance and from the opposite direction. This time it was ten miles. The boys took the trolley and rode to the outskirts of the city, where again they said farewell to their birds and worried all the way home for fear they would not all return. But this time every bird was inside the loft long before the boys reached home, and Miss Mary, who had kept watch for them, reported that they had not all come in one flock, but that a big grizzle-colored bird had led, being several minutes ahead of a black, which was second. Third had come the red-checked cock, which again sat a long time on the roof, and after that they had come so fast that she could not remember.

Something had happened this time to break up the flock. Those with initiative broke away from the rest, were more independent, and sought to find home by themselves, depending on no other bird.

So that was a genuine satisfaction. And they were particularly delighted because the grizzle was among the youngest, having been one of the third lot hatched and raised by the nurse pigeons. Such a rapid homecoming prophesied well for his future.

Another week went by. This time the whole flock was taken again in another direction, across the river on the ferry-boat. Here was the first real test. Crossing water is something that a timid bird will not do, and it looked as if they were likely to lose some this time surely.

The boys took the trolley to the subway, and the subway to the ferry. They rode on the upper deck at the rear of the boat, until they came to the other side of the river. Then, just before the boat docked, they liberated their flock. Some of the birds swooped down as soon as they were clear of the boat. Over the water they flew, several just skimming the surface. Some climbed for altitude. It was new to them, and at once the flock seemed to split up into many smaller flocks. Then they flew up, up, up, ever higher and higher. And to the delight of the boys, most of them headed straight across the broad expanse of the river, showing no fear at all. Over the river they flew and disappeared into the haze of smoke on the other side.

Then the cumbersome ferry moved slowly

out of its slip, back across the river on its many-thousandth trip, and the eager boys again took the subway and hurried toward home.

This time they did not find things so satisfactory as they had before. Instead of twenty-eight birds in the loft, there were only fifteen. However, it had been but an hour since they were liberated and while there was life there was hope. So they stayed there hopeful but rather downcast, especially since this time Grizzle had not yet come. After some fifteen minutes a whirr of wings was heard above, then the pattering of feet on the roof, the tinkling of the wires of the trap, and a sixteenth bird was added. After a few minutes more birds returned, and by the end of two hours there were twenty-five, Grizzle among them. By evening all the birds were home, so the boys felt greatly relieved.

"You know," said Dick, as they were saying good night, "I was banking on Grizzle to be first. I surely do wish I could have known just what every bird did after we let them out."

"Yes, I'd give a lot too, but I'll bet Blackie went off to see the sights, since she knew she was so near home," said Bill. It was easy

to see which pigeon he favored. And Bud had
his favorite too; a long, slim-built bird which
was red-grizzle in color, but so nearly white
that she was known as Whitie. Whitie,
Blackie and Grizzle were the favorites—there
was no use denying it.

Chapter IX

A GREAT TEST FOR THE BIRDS

Summer had now come. No more school
for two months! What a happy thought!
Now they would have more time to spend with
the homers. But with the finishing of school
the Crampton family went to the country and
that meant that Dick went too. It was hard
to tear himself away from the pigeons, but his
father had promised to bring him to town
with him frequently, and that made it a little
easier. The Cramptons' country place was
twenty-six miles away, over in New Jersey,
but his father commuted every day except
Saturdays and Sundays, and it was a simple
matter for Dick to come.

Now Bill and Bud were left to take the
birds on their training flights and to look after
them. But that was only fun.

The next training fly for the birds was for
fifteen miles, and they had to cross both of
the rivers and Manhattan Island as well, but
again all of them eventually returned. Now
it is very likely that had these birds come from

poorer stock not nearly so many would have come home even from the first fly. But these were of great stock, and that accounted for the difference.

One day when Dick came home, the boys persuaded him to get his father to help him carry all the birds out to the country with them. His father quickly agreed. This meant a harder trial for the homers. It was arranged that Dick was to liberate them at seven o'clock in the morning. So all three set their watches exactly alike. The boys would be waiting, and it was expected that they would see some birds by eight, or nine at the latest.

Morning found all three boys dressed at an unusually early hour. Dick was up even before his father, who had to rise early to catch his train. Bud and Bill were about at six. It was hard for them to eat breakfast. The food didn't taste particularly good, but they choked it down. They had a fine system of waking up too, so that they could call one another and yet not disturb the rest of the neighborhood by their shouting. This was a little telephone from one room to another, and the tinkling of its bell aroused each boy.

This was the very first time that any of them had actually seen the birds returning home from a fly, so they had reason to be ex-

cited. It was a balmy morning. An idea occurred to them. "What is the difference,"
they asked, "whether we are in the loft or not?
Let's go up on the roof of Bud's house and
watch. That will be much more exciting."
And so at half-past seven they went up on
Bud's roof, and leaning against a chimney
they scanned the western horizon.

It was seven-forty-five when one of them
heard a noise down below at Pigeon City.
He nudged the other. They both looked, and
there to their astonishment was Grizzle. For
a brief moment he sat on the roof, and in the
next he had bolted through the wires of the
trap. Intent though they had been, they had
not seen him come.

"Say, fellow," said Bill to Bud, "we've got
to look sharper than we have been looking.
We would never be much use as sentries, for
the enemy could slip right past us."

"How do you s'pose he ever got by without
our seeing?" asked Bud.

"It doesn't make any difference—he *did* it,
and that shows we must be blind," said Bill.

Now they looked more steadily and carefully. The sun was at their backs and they
could see clearly except for the smoke haze.
But this time as they watched very intently,
they saw a glorious sight. Out of the haze

emerged a graceful flier winging its way straight as an arrow directly toward them. Oh, how the shivers crept up and down their backs! What emotion they felt! Here was their own little bird coming home to them. They hugged each other in joy. Over their heads it flew, then circled, and dropped down to Pigeon City. It was Whitie.

Now another bird, this time a blue. Then a third and soon a fourth. It was almost as if they had kept in sight of one another. But they were not in a flock; each had flown independently. By nine o'clock twenty-five of their fliers had passed overhead and gone in the front door of their home. And by three o'clock in the afternoon two more returned. One bird never came back. The boys felt grieved, but on the whole were very well satisfied with the results.

The next fly was unique. Bill's father, through his work, knew a captain of a great ocean liner. One day this captain visited Mr. Brighton and stayed to dinner. Of course he was introduced to Pigeon City. It was a genuine treat to meet the boys and to see their enthusiasm. They told him all about the training flies.

Before he left, the captain offered to take the birds with him on the ship which sailed the next morning, and to liberate them at Sandy Hook, the last bit of land that the ship passes until it greets the shores of Europe.

"It will be no trouble at all. You must see that the birds are delivered to the ship before she sails. I will have the first mate let them loose, or I will do it myself," he promised.

That was a great chance. Early the next morning Bill and Bud were up and on their way, taking their twenty-seven homers in the same two boxes in which they had carried them so many times before. Out on the pier they went to the gang-plank of the ship and asked for the captain. He came down and welcomed them cordially. He wanted to show them about the ship, but there was not sufficient time.

"Now please don't forget the pigeons, will you?" begged Bill. "Let them out at Sandy Hook and throw the old boxes away—they are worn out." Then they said good-by and asked the captain to come and see them again when he returned.

From Sandy Hook to Pigeon City was little further than from Dick's summer place to Brooklyn. But it would take the boat several hours to get there, so the boys hardly expected a bird to return before noon; but they were up on the roof at ten o'clock waiting, and this time they resolved that no pigeon would get home unnoticed.

Noon came and no pigeons. The day was cloudless and not too hot. Two o'clock came, and still no pigeons, and the boys were almost sick with anxiety. Three o'clock came, and no birds yet. Miss Mary Gardner had volunteered to go out and look into the coop occasionally to be sure that none had returned without the boys' seeing.

Then Bill's mother came out into the back yard and hoo-hooed. "Come down—there is a message for you, Bill, a radiogram. Hurry up!"

"A radiogram! Something must be wrong! It must be from the captain about the pigeons!" It was.

PASSED SANDY HOOK LATER THAN EX-
PECTED SHALL I LIBERATE IF NOT MUST
CARRY PIGEONS TO EUROPE RADIO RUSH
CAPT JACOBS　　S S HOLLANDER

"What shall we do, Mother?" asked Bill. "By the time we can reach him the ship will be way out at sea. What shall we do?"

"I don't know, son, but make up your minds quickly," answered Mrs. Brighton.

"Let's say yes, Bill," urged Bud. "It will be weeks before the ship comes back. The birds will fly toward the land. Surely they won't go out to sea. It's a good day and there are five hours left before dark."

Mrs. Brighton had kept the telegraph boy waiting. So they quickly wrote a radio message.

CAPT JACOBS
  S S HOLLANDER AT SEA
   LIBERATE AT ONCE

WILLIAM

The boy dashed off on his bicycle as fast as he could ride, for he had a fellow-feeling and had heard what was said.

Soon afterward, Captain Jacobs took the boxes up to the upper deck of the great liner and removed the tops, and instantly the birds were on their way. A crowd of passengers had gathered to see the start. By this time the *Hollander* was thirty miles out in the ocean, far beyond sight of land. So now the Pigeon City homers had a real task before them.

With mind-pictures dancing in their heads the boys waited an hour, and then wearily climbed up to the roof and again waited. The sun was in their eyes now, but they didn't mind; they were there to see some great homers return, and now they half-wished that

they had asked the Captain to carry the birds
over to Europe and back. But they were good
sports and they waited, waited, waited, almost
an age it seemed, after having already waited
nearly the whole day.

Bill pulled out his watch. "If he liberated
them at a quarter-past three, they ought to be

here by five, or perhaps sooner. It depends
on the wind, I suppose."

It was just four o'clock.

"Boys!" again called Mrs. Brighton.

"Yes, Mother," answered Bill over the edge
of the roof. "More hard luck?"

"No, you needn't come down this time. It's
another message from Captain Jacobs, and I
opened it. It says that he liberated them at
three-twenty-two, thirty-one miles at sea."

"Thirty-one miles at sea! Ye gods! They

will never get home," said Bud. "That means between fifty-five and sixty miles from here. It will take them an age. Oh, why did we tell him to let them go?"

"Why? Why?" said Bill scornfully. "Haven't you any more confidence than that in our birds? I believe that every single one is coming home."

"I sure hope you're right. Well, let's keep watching. It might be that one will surprise us and get home like an express train, mile a minute."

"Hey, what's that?" suddenly Bill almost shouted. "Look! look! Nope, it's just a church-steeple pigeon, not ours at all."

Then more waiting. This time it was Bill who caught a punch in the ribs from the point of Bud's elbow, and this time it was no false alarm. It was a Pigeon City flier, and most certainly it was Blackie who seemed to fly right out of the sun. Close after her followed Whitie, and a few minutes later came Grizzle. Then more and more followed until it seemed that all were home.

The overjoyed boys dashed down to Pigeon City and counted just twenty-five stalwart birds in the loft. They were happy boys, as you can imagine! As they stood admiring, something caught Bud's eye.

"Look, what's that on the leg of Red-Check?"

"It looks as if it were tied there." Then going in and catching the bird, Bud exclaimed, "It is! It's a note!" He unfolded it. "For you. Read it!"

"Gosh," said Bill, "it is, and it's from Captain Jacobs."

Dear Bill:

I am the sorriest man in the world to cause you boys so much trouble and anxiety. But I couldn't help it. Everything was against us and we were late at Sandy Hook. I am waiting for your radio message now, and take this opportunity to write you, feeling sure that if you say the word, you are confident your birds will come home safely. When you read this, I am sure you will understand that I did not forget you, and I entrust my letter to this little winged messenger.

I hope you won't regret letting me take your birds, and anyway I will try to make it right with you.

Good-by and good luck!

Christian V. Jacobs.

"Where did he ever find such light, thin paper? Say, he's a good scout, isn't he? I hope he comes back to see us again," exclaimed Bill.

"What do you suppose he means when he says he will make it right with us?" asked Bud.

"I couldn't guess; all we can do is to wait and see."

The next morning another pigeon returned, but for many days they looked in vain for the last.

the door at the country through which they were speeding. Bud was glad to help unload the baggage at the stations at which they stopped—a trunk here and some packages there. At one station they unloaded a crate containing a small calf, and at another a crate in which there was a hunting dog. This was all much more interesting than sitting in the stuffy passenger car.

When the train arrived at Bud's destination he put his head out of the door and there, down the platform a little way, were Dick and another boy waiting. Bud waved and they came running to help him unload his suitcase and the box of homers, and then they all got into a waiting bus which took them to the house where Dick was spending the summer.

On the way Bud told them how he had agreed to liberate the birds as soon as possible so as not to keep Bill waiting too long for them to return. As soon as they got to Dick's, therefore, they stepped out on the lawn and prepared to open the box. Dick called his mother and his aunt and sister, and then the boys let out the birds that were on one side of the partition. Bud was just getting ready to liberate the rest, when Dick caught his hand.

"Wait a minute, Bud," said he. "How

would it be if we took a few of them with us
on our trip and let one go every day with a
message on its leg? That would keep Bill
posted on our doings and he would enjoy reading the letters we send him. I wish he could
have come along, too."

"By Jove, that's an idea. Get some thin
paper and a pencil and we'll begin right now.
You write him the note. He'll be glad to have
it from you because I have been with him all
summer so far."

So Dick wrote, and in the little note he told
Bill that they would be gone for six days and
would take six birds with them, letting all the
others go with this one that had the message
on its leg.

As soon as the note was carefully tied on
the leg of a big, whitish-colored bird, all of
the remaining except six were liberated. The
first lot was still circling high up in the air
when the second flock started to climb for
altitude. In no time they had been swallowed
up in the first. Then all of them moved off
in the direction of Brooklyn.

At home Bill was watching for the return.
The birds knew the way from past experience,
and came back in a very short time. Bill
found the note, too, and was delighted at the

thoughtfulness of his friends. Now he would have a daily reminder, and an account of the fun he was missing.

In the meanwhile the campers were making preparations to start. The automobile was all ready. A small crate for the six homers was improvised, with a can in the corner for drinking water, a bag of grain was obtained from the store, and the party of boys was ready to be off.

The car was pretty well packed with their luggage. The tents took up not a little room, and the rest of the things and the pigeons, to say nothing of the big box of food for the boys, filled the car to overflowing.

Next day at ten o'clock, Bill went out into Pigeon City. He sat waiting for a trusted messenger to bring him news of the camping trip. True to form, in fluttered the bird. Bill was waiting by the entrance, and as the pigeon alighted inside of the loft, he took the very thin tissue paper from one of its legs. But in so doing, he noticed that there was a piece upon the other leg too. This he also removed, and then he began to read. The first sheet he opened said at the top, "Read other sheet first." Thereupon he began on the other sheet. It read:

DEAR BILL:

We all wish you were here with us. The trip was great. We made fine time. Paul just about made the car fly. We nearly got arrested by a motorcycle cop for speeding, but when he caught up to us I guess he remembered that he had been a boy himself. Really the pigeons saved us, because when he looked in the box and saw them and when we told him our intention of releasing a bird each day, he said that he used to have homers once himself and winked at us, but he gave us a good scare and told us to go slower after this.

We went over the Great Bear Mountain Bridge. Boy, it's a knockout! Take that trip whenever you can. We went right northeast after we got over the bridge, and stayed in New York State, but we are pretty close to Connecticut. We got here at just the right time and pitched our two pup-tents and piled up some rocks for a swell fireplace and everything is perfect. The lake we are on is very wide and long. It's a corker. Gosh, I wish you were here. Now look on the other leg.

Paul and Jim—he's the older fellow, our chaperon—slept in one tent and Dick and I slept in the other. Really none of us slept so well as we might have, but nobody would admit it. Anyway, we had the box of pigeons down at the foot of our tent so they would be safe. They kept

cooing all night and what was worse, the bloom-
ing mosquitoes nearly ate us alive. When we
pulled our heads under the blankets to keep them
off, we nearly melted, it was so hot. Finally we
got on to a way of putting our piece of mosquito
netting over the front end of our tent, and then
after a while when the mosquitoes that were left
inside finished eating, we got to sleep. It was so
nice and cool early this morning that we hated to
get up, but Jim says that campers should get up
early and as we didn't want to be poor sports we
got up. Hope this message gets home O.K. I'm
sure it will. Will send another to-morrow via
pigeon mail. But if the weather is too bad we
won't send any.

YOUR FRIENDS BUD AND DICK.

Bill was delighted with the message. But
he was just as glad that he hadn't had to con-
tend with the mosquitoes. He was even more
eager for a message the next day. And it
came as promptly as the first.

DEAR BILL:

Oh, boy, we are tired. I guess we're going to
take a nap this afternoon and be sure of that
much sleep. But first I'll tell you about yesterday. It was very quiet. We went up the lake
about three miles and got a canoe from a farmer
and we all paddled it down here. Bud and I
decided that we don't like canoes, they are too

shaky. We nearly spilled out several times. We were worried all the time for fear some animal would get in and kill the homers, which we had had to leave. But they were all right, and we paddled around a lot and had a great time. We went swimming three times. Bud got so sunburned that he's all red and it pained him all night. Right out in front of our tent is the fireplace, and nearby we had placed a box upside down, with our food under it. It would keep dry that way, and we had a poncho spread over the whole top. Well, last night we went to bed soon after dark, to make up sleep. Bud couldn't sleep much because of his sunburn, but I dropped right off. The pigeons were all nice and quiet and Bud was sleeping after a fashion, when about two o'clock in the morning we were all suddenly awakened. (*Continued on other leg.*)

For a long while we didn't know what had happened. We all woke up. We had made an agreement that if either one of us wanted to wake the other up he would just put his hand softly on the other fellow's face. Bud was just reaching for my face as I was for his and when our hands met we got an awful fright. If we had been girls we probably would have screamed. It was terrible. Well, when we found we were both awake that gave us courage, so we got the flashlight and looked out. We could see our provisions strewn all about and could hear a funny noise. I was

going out but I thought it might be a bear or a
skunk and didn't like the idea. So we called to
the other fellows and they didn't know what to
do either. Anyhow we all got up, and there was
a great big clumsy-looking animal waddling away.
We put our lights on him and he went toward a
tree near the tents. We didn't know what it was
at first, but we know now! We know, because
just as he started up the tree Bud kicked him to
keep him down till Jim got the ax. Poor Bud
yelled *"Ouch!"* and we saw that he had kicked a
porcupine! We didn't bother it any more, but
just let it climb the tree. Then we tried to pull
the quills out of Bud's ankle. We got a few with
our fingers, but most of them had to be pulled with
our teeth, and some were in deep and hurt terribly. But he was surely game. Sunburn and porcupine! Poor Bud!

Anyhow we found that the beast had spoiled
most of our bacon—they love salt—and had
messed everything up awfully. After we went
back to bed we heard him again but this time the
light frightened him away. No more room, will
write to-morrow.

DICK AND BUD.

Bill had a good laugh. Then he took the
letters in and showed them to his parents and
Bud's mother and Gramp and finally to some
of the fellows in the neighborhood. So they
all had much to talk about.

Next day was very stormy. Bill wondered what his friends were doing to amuse themselves, but the following day he found out. This time a black pigeon arrived with a message:

DEAR BILL:

Two days have gone since we sent you a message. The days are fine but the nights are not so good. If it's not mosquitoes, or porcupines, it's thunderstorms. But we are all happy and wish you were here too. Didn't send a message yesterday because it rained so hard. But it didn't matter. The day before, it rained in the afternoon so there wasn't much news. We just fished and took it easy, and had a great time. Paul had a little Victrola which we played. Next time we need food we are going to paddle up to the other end of the lake for it instead of driving. The day was awfully warm Wednesday too, until it began to drizzle, and at night a hard thunder shower came up. The lightning must have struck a tree very near us because the flash and the clap came at the same instant and there was a terrific splintering sound. I never heard such a long storm, and none of us ever knew it to rain so hard. The rain drove right through the tents, and we had to keep our rubber blankets over the provisions and the pigeons, so we all got wet.

Anyhow when the morning finally did arrive we crawled out and I recalled how to make a thatched

hut from having read it in my old guide book.
So we peeled off and worked right in the rain for
a long time yesterday and— (*See other leg.*)

First we cut a stick to go between two trees.
Then we put a lot of smaller sticks from this, slop-
ing down to the ground, and cut hemlock branches
and thatched them all over the back, or roof, of
our lean-to. We made it thick and it kept the
rain out well. Next we built a fire in front and
strung up a line under the lean-to and hung our
wet things over it, and they dried out pretty
quickly. We have had trouble with the pigeons
too. There is that big red-check that you remember was such a bully. He gets right over the
water and won't let the rest near it, and he tries
to take all the food. He looks so big and strong
that I would depend on him to get home quickly,
so we're keeping him in case of an emergency,
which surely won't come as long as we are prepared.

Last night we had our first real sleep. After
the rain it was cool and nice and we are all getting
used to the strange surroundings, so we slept
better. Now we're going for a dip. Wish you
were here.

Bud and Dick.

Bill was certainly enjoying the messages.
Only two more would come at the most. Friday morning's had been the best yet. So on

Saturday he went to the loft to see what would turn up. Each morning it had been the custom to let the homers have a good fly, but this week the plan was abandoned because Bill wanted to have the birds which the campers liberated come in as soon as they arrived home. By ten o'clock a blue-checked bird arrived looking as if he had flown through a storm. Bill, who was eager to discover the cause of the delay and to hear the news, unfolded the one message it bore as quickly as he could. Instead of finding the message on nice smooth rice-paper like the others, he found that the paper was wrinkled all over and badly warped. It read:

DEAR BILL:
We have been in an awful fix. Late yesterday afternoon we decided to go to town at the other end of the lake and buy some food. We had paddled there and were returning when a fierce black cloud came up. Almost before we knew it the rain and wind began. We paddled as fast as we could toward an island but before we could make it we tipped over, and luckily found that we were in shallow water and could wade ashore. We had brought the pigeons with us and it certainly was good luck that the box floated, or they would have been drowned. Anyway we reached the island and here we are getting dried out. Jim

Bud and Dick sent Bill a message each day

had a waterproof match-box and as soon as the storm was over we made a fire and spent the night here. Now I am writing this and will tie it on the leg of the blue-check. We had to dry out the paper. I can't write more now as we are getting ready to push off for camp. Will send one more message to-morrow and that will be the last. Bet you are glad you didn't come and are safe at home.

BUD AND DICK.

Next day it was Red-Check who brought a message. He too looked worse for wear after the wetting he had received, but it had not seemed to slow him up. He came earlier than most of the other birds had arrived. In fact, he was in the loft when Bill went to feed his charges in the morning. The message read:

DEAR BILL:

We were probably back at camp before you got our letter. Everything was all right and the porcupines had not bothered anything. When Mr. Hubbard saw the fire on the island last night he guessed who it was and came down here to see if we were safe. He seemed to feel badly that he had ever let us have such a shaky canoe and made us come home with him and have dinner. I suppose you think that we didn't eat! Eating is what we have done better than anything else since we arrived here. Mrs. Hubbard served a great meal and after our experience on the island it tasted better than any meal I ever ate.

And didn't we sleep last night! I never knew a thing after I crawled in until Jim woke us up, and Bud says that he didn't either. The other fellows are packing the car with our luggage while I am writing this. Here's hoping Red-Check gets home with it. We almost decided to let Grizzle go also, and would if it weren't for the hawks. We don't know whether you got the other messages we sent, but hope so. Every little while we hear a hawk scream, and yesterday we saw two of them. So we are going to take Grizzle with us as far as my summer home and let him go there.

There's a big mountain twenty miles from here that we can see, and we are going to climb it before we go home. I will be home some time late to-night or to-morrow morning. So long till then.

BUD AND DICK.

At two o'clock Bill was sitting in his room on the top floor reading. Miss Mary Gardner knocked on the back door, and Mrs. Brighton called to Bill to come downstairs.

"Bill," said Miss Mary, when he arrived, "did you know that a pigeon had just come home? I happened to be looking out of the window and saw him alight and go in."

"Was he a dark, mottled bird?" asked Bill.

"Yes, I'm sure I have seen him many times before."

"Let's hurry," said Bill. "Something must have gone wrong." He dashed out to the coop with Miss Mary and his mother following. There he found that Grizzle had come home, so he took the message from his leg. It read:

Bill, for goodness' sake help us. When we were on top of the mountain Jim was bitten on the hand by a rattlesnake. We have given him first aid and have put a twister on his wrist. It will take two or three hours to get him to the nearest hospital, wherever that is. I ran ahead to write this message and send it via Grizzle. They are bringing Jim slowly down to the car so the poison won't spread much, and when they get here we will go to Brewster, which probably has a hospital. Now won't you please telephone to the big New York hospitals and try to locate some rattlesnake anti-venom serum and get them to send it to Brewster or to the nearest hospital? We will be there. We are afraid that the little hospitals won't be supplied. If you can get the serum there quickly maybe we can save Jim's life.

DICK.

Bill rushed to the house and asked his father to telephone to the nearest large hospital.

After getting in touch with the doctor in charge, Mr. Brighton learned that they had a supply and also that there was a hospital at Brewster. He went with his son directly to the New York hospital, got the serum, and then proceeded to the Grand Central Terminal, where they waited an hour for a train. Then Mr. Brighton put his son on the train and said good-by.

It was fortunate that the trusty grizzle bird had been liberated. The boys had been a long while making their way down the mountain. Well they knew that if Jim were hurried it would go hard with him. But bad though it was, the worst was to come. They planned to stop at the nearest farmhouse and telephone to Brewster. So they got started along the lonesome, narrow, muddy road which ran by the foot of the mountain.

They were making good time when it became necessary to turn out for another car which approached. As they did so they felt the wheels on the right side slip and sink into the mud. The other car went past easily and on down the road.

Now the boys were in a predicament. Only three of them could do the pushing since Jim couldn't exert himself. The pain in his arm was acute. At times he lost consciousness, causing the boys great alarm. The three pushed and tugged, jacked the wheels and put stones under them, but it was half an hour before they were going again. Then it was some time before they reached the first house.

Paul ran to the house and asked the farmer to please telephone to the hospital for them and say they were on the way.

The eighteen remaining miles to Brewster seemed endless. Over and over they asked each other about the homer which had flown unknowingly on his errand of mercy. *Had* he arrived safely? *Had* Bill seen him come? *Had* they been able to get the serum? *Was* Bill on his way?

Once at the Brewster Hospital the medical force did what they could to counteract the action of the snake's poison. They had no serum and telephoned at once to New York asking that a supply be sent. When they learned that there were no more trains for several hours they ordered the material sent by special car. They were unwilling to place any dependence on the pigeon.

Bud and Dick and Paul were not allowed in the room with Jim and the doctors. They were pushed aside and treated as boys of their ages might expect to be treated. They sat in

the waiting room—waiting—waiting—hoping
—for Bill. And their confidence in Grizzle
was not to be shaken. Less than half an hour
after they arrived at the hospital, Bill dashed
from a taxi up the steps of the hospital. He
found the boys at once, and they took him up
to the room where the hospital staff were
working over Jim. Then they handed the
serum to the doctor in charge.

"Boys," said he, "this is simply wonderful!
How did you do it? You have probably saved
your friend's life. He is in grave danger and
there would have been little hope without the
serum."

"Oh," answered Bill, somewhat proudly,
"we can depend on our pigeons." Then turning to the boys he said, "None but the best for
Pigeon City. That's once when our slogan
was justified!"

"None but the best!" they answered, and
shaking hands with the doctor, they took their
departure.

Chapter XI

PIGEON IMMIGRATION

SUMMER was passing quickly. More training flies were arranged but all at a greater distance than the one from the ship. Three weeks had passed since then, and one of these weeks would never be forgotten by the boys.

Then had come the fly from close to Philadelphia, when they lost two more of their flock. For a long while this puzzled the boys, but finally an old homing-pigeon man told them that he always lost most heavily when he liberated his birds from that particular place. "Perhaps they can see the city of Philadelphia in the distance," he said, "and are attracted to it. They may spend so much time deciding that it is not their home that darkness overtakes them. Thus they frequently stray into pigeon coops and are caught, never to be liberated."

At any rate, on that particular fly, although it was but seventy-five miles away, only eighteen of their birds returned during the day, and the rest arrived the next morning; that is, except the two that never returned. And again Blackie was the first to arrive. Her time was exactly ninety minutes, which was fast indeed.

Every morning it was their custom to count the fliers. There were twenty-four birds, two dozen, a number easy to remember. And if you had been as well acquainted with those pigeons as the boys were, you too would have noticed at a glance if the numbers had changed. Once in a while a stray dropped in and he was instantly spotted by the first boy to arrive at the loft. To most people one pigeon looks about like the next one he sees. But to the pigeon fancier there is as much difference between his birds as there is between the different people whom he knows. Just as the shepherd can see great differences in his sheep because he knows them so well, the pigeon fancier likewise knows his pigeons; his eye is trained.

So it happened that one morning when Bud was feeding the birds, he thought things didn't look right. He counted quickly. His eyes traveled over the flock as they were all eating on the floor, and he caught sight of a bird which had been familiar to him in the past but which he had not seen for some time—the silver hen.

"Oh, you little beauty!   Where have you been?" said Bud.   "Let's see, you were lost from the ship and we thought you were drowned.   Where have you been, where *have* you been?   Are you thin, I wonder?"

Then he caught her and felt, but instead she had grown fat.   And as he held her with her feet between his first and second fingers, something unusual seemed to be there.   He looked. There was a message, which he quickly took off and read.   First he looked at the signature.   Captain Jacobs' again.   The message said:

DEAR WILLIAM:·
I hope that if this pretty bird ever gets to her home you will find her and read this before I arrive.   After I liberated the pigeons, they went off toward home.   Several hours later, when it was nearly dark, this little beauty came back and alighted on the ship.   When it was dark, I sent a sailor to catch her.   We have kept her for a pet ever since, and she has behaved very well.   I shall let her go as soon as the ship docks.   Please tell your father that I shall be over to see him tomorrow evening.   Have you any room in Pigeon City for some more pigeons?   I have been almost

sick fearing that the others never got home. I hope that you will have good news for me. Please remember me very kindly to your friends.

CHRISTIAN V. JACOBS.

Bud started to look for Bill and found him coming out to see the pigeons. "Look what I have!" he said by way of greeting. "Tell your father that Captain Jacobs is coming to see him to-morrow night. The silver hen has just come back and brought this message from him." Bill read the message, and then went in to tell his father.

"What'll we do with the silver hen?" asked Bill. "She can't be much good or she'd have come home and not gone back to the boat."

"Well, yes, but she had some sense to find the boat after it had gone further away, too," said Bud.

"That's right. Let's keep her, and if she isn't any good she won't come back from the races."

That day and the next went by rather slowly. In the evening Captain Jacobs arrived in a taxicab. He came into the house empty-handed, and the boys who were waiting behind the curtains noticed that the taxi did not drive away at once, as taxis usually

do.   The Captain sat down in his leisurely
fashion.

"Well, what are you going to do with me,
boys?" he asked.   "Was I the means of losing all your pigeons?   If so, I surely am
sorry."

"There is nothing for you to be sorry about.
Right now we haven't lost a single one, but
until this morning we had been missing just
one, the silver hen," answered Bill.

"Yes, the silver one.   And did you get my
message?"

"You bet we did.   What did you mean by
asking if we had room for any more pigeons?"

"Just that," replied Captain Jacobs.
"Have you?"

"Oh, yes, we have room, plenty of it, but
we have made a resolution to allow only the
very best homing pigeons to become residents
of Pigeon City.   We are very exclusive.   This
city is not like other cities.   Only the best for
Pigeon City!   That's our motto."

"And who, pray, is the judge of which are
best?" asked the Captain.

"We are."

"And by what method do you choose?"

"By the family records.   We are very careful to inspect the families and to see that there

is no poor heredity. Every citizen of Pigeon City is the highest grade we can find. We can't take any chances."

"Good idea, excellent idea!" said their friend. "I should like to live in a city of humans like that, myself. They ought to make good neighbors. But now here is the question: would you be willing to accept any immigrants to your exclusive city?"

"Well," said Bill who was doing most of the talking, "I would say offhand that we might. Our population is not so large as we need, and we could increase it to good advantage. But, as I said, the immigrants would have to pass high tests,—they would have to come from only the most able families."

"Then," said Captain Jacobs, "go out and tell that taxi-man to bring in those boxes. I have some immigrants that I think will find a welcome in Pigeon City."

Gleefully the boys both rushed to beckon to the taxi-man, who responded by bringing two boxes in. He set them down in the hall, took his fee from Captain Jacobs, and departed.

"Pigeons!" exclaimed Bill.

"Pigeons!" said Bud. "A lot of them too."

"Where did you get them, Captain?" asked Bill.

"Now look here, don't you know the old

saying, 'Never look a gift horse in the mouth to see how old he is'?   Well, never look a gift pigeon over too carefully."

"Oh, but this is different," said Bill.   "It is all right to look them over and to ask questions about them, when we are so particular about our immigrants as we must be.   And then again it makes a difference whether we have to feed them for a year, too."

"Yes, you are right," said Captain Jacobs. "Now, joking aside, let me tell you what I have brought you.   The larger box contains pigeons that I got in Germany.   And this is their history.   When I let your pigeons go, a kindly gentleman came to see me and we became well acquainted.   I explained my misgivings to him and told him about your radio message.   He admired your pluck.   'Those boys will develop a great flock, I am sure,' he said.   We talked things over and I decided that it was very possible that I had been the means of losing all of your birds.   Then when the silver hen came back to the ship I was sure I had.   Now it developed that this gentleman has a son who owns one of the greatest lofts of homers in Germany.   So I was given a letter of introduction to him.   What it said I don't know, but I do know that he gave me all but two of the birds in that largest box.

Perhaps they are not his best but he says that they are as good as the best. But here's what I did: I asked to see his very best, and when he showed them to me I bought the best pair from among those. Both have flown over a thousand miles in fast time."

"Oh!" exclaimed both boys in awe.

"Then," went on Captain Jacobs, "he gave me a letter of introduction to a fancier in Antwerp, Belgium, who he said had the best there. When I got there I showed him some American money and was able to buy all of the best that he had. But he said he could buy some more from his friends. So that's that. And since money was not too plentiful with either man, I fancy they were not keeping poor homers, but had only the finest. When you come to look you will find several pairs of squabs among the lot which have never been out of their home, and I was told that they would consider home to be the place to which they first become accustomed. Put them with your fliers and that will show you what kind of stock I have brought. At any rate it was the best I could do."

"Thank you a thousand times," said Bud.

"Thanks, Captain Jacobs," said Bill. "But how are we ever going to repay you?"

"Just let me come and see the progress you

are making once in a while," the Captain answered. "That will repay me more than I
deserve. Now you fellows run along and let
me talk with Bill's dad."

Out to Pigeon City they went carrying the
big consignment.

The lights were turned on, for Mr. Hitchcock, being in the electrical business, had wired
the loft and put a light in each room. The
German birds were turned loose in one of the
pens. There were twelve of them, including
the best pair, which they could recognize because they were in a special compartment in
the box. The boys put the Belgian pigeons in
the other breeding room. Of these there were
eighteen. Several pair were already mated.
The eight young ones were then transferred
to the room for the fliers.

The old birds unfortunately could never be
let out, but must be kept for breeding purposes
only. Had they been given their freedom
they would have tried to get home; of course
they could not fly across the ocean and so
might have perished at sea. Therefore all of
their lives they must be kept in the enclosure.

Next morning Dick came home from the
country for good. He was rather envious to
think that he had not been there when Captain
Jacobs brought the birds.

The rows of nest-boxes in Pigeon City

All three spent an hour in the morning shopping for a good substantial book in which to keep records. Then they went out to Pigeon City and sat there as still as mice watching the pigeons. When they did move it was with slow motions, never jerky. Each boy sat on a little stool, and one was in each room. By watching in this way it was easy to see which birds were mated, and that was what they wanted to know.

The rows of nest-boxes in Pigeon City were of course the pigeons' homes. The top row was First Avenue, the next was Second Avenue, and so forth. Then each street up and down had its special name, and each nest-box or home was equipped with a nice door. As soon as a boy would see by their actions that a certain pair were mated he would at once catch them and put them into a home. And after this was done he would note the band numbers and enter the facts in the new book, thus creating a permanent record.

The work was finished after two hours. Bill, who was in the room with the fliers, saw that several of the American cocks were paying attention to the hen pigeons among the newcomers, and also that the cock birds of the immigrants were paying attention to the American hens. He also found that two pair of the first hatching of the original birds were mated, and made a note of that.

The old records, too, were all transferred to the new big record book, and after further observation the boys went out to play in a vacant lot nearby. There they kicked a football and got their quota of exercise for the day.

The new young birds were let out to fly as soon as they had become accustomed to Pigeon City. After a few days of experimenting one could scarcely tell them from the rest of the birds, as they flew. The flock looked much larger now, and the boys liked to see them circling far up above the housetops.

But it would have been unfair to put these newcomers into the races later without first having given them some intensive training. This time, in order to test their mettle, they were taken to the second training point two miles away, and seven of the eight came back very quickly. Then they were taken over on the old ferry-boat trip, and again they returned. Later they were taken to Tottenville on the furthermost end of Staten Island, and again they came home in good time. Seven birds to survive out of eight was not a bad record!

Chapter XII

ENTERED FOR THE CENTURY

THE BROOKLYN HOMING PIGEON CLUB boasted over fifty members. It was the newest of the clubs to be organized. These men had now begun to train their birds together. Although they could have taken them individually, they found it less expensive to ship in a lot and to have the express-agent at some depot liberate the birds. This continued for some little time while the boys were training their birds by themselves. Finally came a 75-mile training fly in which hundreds of homers were shipped by the club. Pigeon City had of course joined the club, and every time the secretary circularized the members he scratched his head and wondered who or what Pigeon City could be. At the meetings, none of which the boys had yet attended, the matter was discussed.

"Does anybody know what Pigeon City is, who owns it, or anything about it?" asked the secretary. "All I know is that the request for membership and bands came in early this

spring and it was written in a boyish hand.
Pigeon City didn't order many bands—only
about thirty, I believe. That is all I can say.
Who knows anything about it?"

Nobody knew a single thing, but one man
said that there were "some kids" who had
come to see him and that they had bought
some eggs from him. "It may be that these
kids call their loft Pigeon City. But I guess
we won't have anything to worry about from
their competition, especially since they haven't
trained their birds. I will say, however, that
they had a chance to have at least two pairs
of mighty fine birds if those eggs I sold them
ever hatched."

"Yes," spoke up another man, "some kids
paid me a call and I let them have a few eggs
too, and some good ones. And they brought
an old man with them when they came to see
me. Maybe he is the brains behind them.
What would three kids know about flying
homers?"

"Well, by Jove, if they learned anything
from my answers to all their questions, they
know something, and that's no joke," replied
the first man. "I never heard so many questions asked in so short a time in my life. And
if my opinion is worth anything the old man

who was with them didn't know as much about pigeons as they did."

"Boys," said another man, "my next-door neighbor once had a lot of fancy pigeons, and I shall never forget the way he used to come home after every show like a whipped dog because the same boys had beaten him again with their fancy pigeons. He was quite relieved to know that they had sold their whole lot and that now he could win. Can it be that these same kids have gone in for homers?"

And so the questioning went on, the speculation, the guesses as to who or what Pigeon City was. Indeed the uncertainty about Pigeon City was worrying the members. Every discussion always wound up the same way: "What's the use of wondering? They couldn't win a race. They haven't trained their birds. And anyway they have only a few"—and so forth and so on.

When the club held its great seventy-five-mile training fly, Pigeon City was not represented, and therefore the club members felt certain that there was no point in even considering this mysterious competition. The members were reassured.

The second Saturday in September was the date set for the first young bird race. The old bird races were over and there had not been a single Pigeon City entry. But now it was their turn to try for coveted honors. Friday night was shipping night. The club rooms, alive with men and dense with tobacco smoke, were piled up with neat carrying boxes filled to the bursting point with pigeons.

In walked three young club members carrying more boxes. This was their first experience at the club.

"Where do we register our birds?" asked one of the three, of the man standing nearest the door.

"Step over to that table and tell the clerk you are here and he will call you when your turn comes." So the three strangers obeyed. After saying that Pigeon City was represented, they retired to the back of the room and sat down.

When they were out of earshot, the clerk motioned to the secretary. "There goes your Pigeon City, just three kids, and you fellows have been worrying over the competition they might furnish. Ha, ha!"

The secretary soon passed the word around, and before long the boys saw many curious glances in their direction. Finally a pleasant-looking man stepped up and shook hands. He turned out to be a man from whom they had purchased several pairs of eggs. "I am Mr. Ross," he said. "Well, fellows, how many birds are you going to enter?"

"Thirty-one," answered Bud.

"What? Where did you get so many?"

"Oh, from all over. You'd be surprised!" answered Dick who was sitting next to him.

"Did the eggs from my birds hatch?"

"Every one."

"Then, by gorry, I believe there are going to be a lot of surprised fellows in this club before noon to-morrow. Have you trained them any?"

"You bet we have! We've been at it all summer. They are good fliers too," put in Bud.

"How many did you lose all told?"

"Four in all."

"Impossible! How far did you take them?"

"Seventy-five miles twice!" said Dick.

"Boys," exclaimed the startled man almost in a whisper, "do me a favor! This is too good to be true. If anybody else asks you anything about your birds, don't tell him a thing. It would please me more than I can tell you to see some smart-alecks drop their jaws to-morrow! If anybody asks you, tell them you have trained your birds some, but don't say how much. The club members are

wondering and speculating as to who you are.
They don't believe that boys can win a race.
Keep them guessing. Good night!" And the
man went home because his birds were already
registered.

"Pigeon City!" called a man in a scornful
voice, almost as if he were wasting his time
calling out the name.

"Here we are," one said when they had
reached the table.

"Well, there's your clock. Know how to
work it?" said the secretary.

"No, sir," said two voices in unison.

"Well, these two slides are pulled back.
You see those holes that they will cover when
they are shut—well, when your birds get
home, if they do, take off the little bands we
are going to put on now, and slip one in one

hole and push the slide over it.   When you do
this a clock in the box will start to go.   Then
when your next birds get home put as many
bands as you want in the next hole and close
that slide and another clock will start.   Most
people put just one band in the second hole.
When both slides are shut, bring the clock here
as soon as you can."

So saying, he asked for the birds.   A dozen
club members stood about the table to witness
the fun, expecting to see a lot of scrub stock.

"Here's one," said Bill, opening his box and
putting his hand in through the corner.   "His
name is Grizzle and he will be among the first
home."

"Sonny," said the secretary, "many a man
before you has made big predictions for his
birds and been sorry afterwards when he found
that a lot of men heard him, as they are hear-
ing you now.   When you make predictions,
better tell just one or two people—then there
won't be so many to laugh when your calculations are upset!"

Bill turned to the other boys and winked.
The man put a narrow, flat bar of aluminum
around the bird's leg.   On the inside was a
number which no one but himself knew and
he recorded this number in a book, together

with the color and sex
number of the band on
   "Next!" called the s
   Another member was
box of males only, a fine,
of water.
   Bill took out another
among the first too," he sa
how many of you hear m
   Another and another
his box was empty. The
and as he came to Blackie,
that here was one that wou
present" when the first bir
   "What on earth are the
asked the man as he came t
never saw bands and nu
Where did they come fro
course referring to the Ger
gian pigeons.
   "Those? Why, those are
swered Dick impulsively.
   "What do you mean, im
strays? No, there wouldn't
the same kind of bands," said
   "Call them immigrants and
We don't know much about t
said Dick.

"You boys are pretty tight-mouthed, aren't you? I bet you can keep a secret."

After the boys had left the club, there was not quite the sense of security that there had been before they came. It began to look to the club members as if Pigeon City was something real after all. Every bird the boys had entered looked business-like. And many of the members stood about the crates and gazed long and steadily at the beautiful feathered creatures. Such a uniformly high-grade lot had seldom been entered.

"I heard one of those kids say," said an old-timer, "that they had entered every young bird they own. I admire their nerve. They are starting right; that is, provided they have trained their flock."

Chapter XIII

THE FIRST RACE

"One hundred miles away! Just think of it!" said Bud to his family at the breakfast table.

"Are you nervous, lad?" asked Gramp.

"Well, just a little," answered Bud. "We surely had those club members buffaloed last night, and after Bill's bragging I hope that we won't have to feel like monkeys. But the thing that makes me feel most—well, you know, sort of uneasy—is that to-day is bad. It is too foggy, and I wouldn't wonder if it rained. Do you suppose that they will let them go if it rains? Say, I hope not."

"I would advise you to call up the club secretary and ask him. He will know," said Gramp. It was now half-past seven. The pigeons were to have been liberated at seven. Bud phoned at once.

"Yes," said the secretary, "they are on the way. I just had a telegram from the station agent that the weather is fine there and so he liberated at seven, exactly as we directed him.

I guess the bad weather is only local. Good luck!"

"He says," reported Bud, "that they are on the way and the weather is good, but when he wished us good luck it didn't sound as if he meant it! I must tell Dick and Bill."

Now excitement reigned. Bud and Bill had watched the birds return from many a training fly during the summer so Dick wanted to go up on the roof and watch. Bud was more than content and agreed to sit in the coop and wait. The weather was becoming thicker. Whereas one would naturally have expected it to get brighter as the morning wore along, it was growing more and more foggy.

"I wish it would rain and clear up this fog," said Dick. "No bird can see through this; they will all have to rely on their sense of direction alone. Here's hoping they don't need to see to know where they are."

"Yes, and on such a day I really don't think the best bird will win; it's more luck than anything else to-day. Don't you think so?" asked Bud. Dick and Bill agreed.

Eight o'clock came, the hour set to start watching, because as they said, if there were a tail wind, the fliers might get home before they knew it. But no such good luck!

Half-past eight came; no pigeons. "Could

hardly expect a bird to go a hundred miles in ninety minutes, Bill," said Dick.

"No, but a bird averaged nearly that speed from one fly," answered his companion.

More time passed. Dick looked at his watch. Nearly nine o'clock! It was beginning to sprinkle. They could not see two blocks away, but the rain would help to get rid of some of the fog. Soon a breeze began to blow. That meant the end of the fog, but it looked bad for the birds, for the wind was partly against them; it was coming from the northwest, while they were southwesterly from Pigeon City. The boys were getting wet. A few minutes longer they watched and then were forced to go down from the roof.

They went to Pigeon City. It was just nine o'clock.

"Easy there! For goodness' sake go easy. They are coming," said Bud in a loud whisper. "I've got one clocked, and which do you think it is?"

"Which? Tell us!"

"One of those Belgian birds," said Bud. "Captain Jacobs brought us good immigrants. Eh, what?"

Now the boys were all sitting still, admiring the great little Belgian homer. One of the youngest birds in the lot, and home first!

"Shh—listen," one whispered. "I heard another alight."

Footsteps on the roof! The tinkling of the trap wires, and another bird home! Bud quickly caught her. This time it proved to be none other than Whitie. And what a bedraggled bird she was!

"Shall I clock her, or shall we wait and get a lot of bands in the second clock?" asked Bud.

"Clock her now, and let's call it a day. There's no telling when another will show up in this fog."

"Wait! Wings! Hear?" Bud waited. In a second, two birds were through the trap. This time a German and the big red-check. Almost more quickly than it takes to tell it, their bands were in the clock and Bud shut the slide. The clock began to tick.

Impetuous boys! Bill was dispatched to the club rooms in the rain. He was the first to arrive. He left the clock with the astonished secretary.

"Four bands in it," he said.

"I don't know whether you won or not, boy, but I will say this, that your mysterious Pigeon City has given somebody an awful rub."

When he got home the rain had stopped. More birds had arrived. By night all but four were accounted for—twenty-seven out of thirty-one. Not so bad!

"Say, fellows, I was the first one at the club rooms, but honest, I haven't got the nerve to call up and ask whether we won. Let's get Gramp to."

Gramp was more than willing. "Who won the race to-day?" he asked. It was then late in the afternoon.

"Can't tell yet," came a voice from the other end of the wire. "It is so close. But we shall have all the figuring and distance allowances worked out, and you will find a notice in the paper to-morrow."

The Sunday paper carried the story:

GREAT PIGEON RACE
FLOWN THROUGH STORM

ONE OF CLOSEST IN YEARS OWING TO
FINE ENTRIES. MYSTERY LOFT
PIGEON CITY FIGURES HIGH!

The order of winners was as follows: First, Oscar C. Ross; second, Pigeon City; third, Pigeon City; fourth, Pigeon City; fifth, Pigeon City; sixth, C. P. Jones; seventh, P. K. Angel; eighth, Wm. O. Doherty. These were far in the lead. The next birds timed were fifteen minutes after any of the above.

Of course there was much gloating. The boys were among the first, very decidedly so. Now they could go to the club with their chins high. But they hadn't won.

"What pleases me, boys," said Bud, "is that no other birds were clocked for fifteen minutes after those. Why, we had twelve birds home before that, so we must have some real homers." They certainly had.

Chapter XIV

ONE HUNDRED AND FIFTY MILES

THE following week after the 100-mile race came the futurity, another 100-mile race in which every member usually entered his best. The 100-mile fly had revealed the outstanding birds. Some fanciers had held back their best fliers for this big event. Fewer birds were shipped and some of the men bet very large sums on their favorites. But the proprietors of Pigeon City would have none of that. They were in the game for the sport only.

Impetuous again, they were going to enter all of their birds, and but for the advice of Gramp they might have done so.

"Fifteen years old! You boys have many years to fly pigeons. Give the poor things a rest. Now don't overdo it, I tell you. You have probably done better than boys have ever done before. Why not lie low this week, and then next week, after the birds have had a rest, come out strong?"

"That's right. Isn't our motto 'None but the best for Pigeon City'?" Dick was talking. "One hundred and fifty miles will tell us more about our birds than a hundred. Let's stay out altogether and then come in strong next week. I'm for that. What do you say?"

"I'm agreed," said Bill. "Why tire them all out and then lose a lot? We won't gain anything. We aren't in this for money. We are going to use this year principally to find out which birds we want for breeders next. None but the best!"

"O.K.," said Bud.

Thus the sturdy Pigeon City fliers had a much-needed rest for an extra week.

One could hardly blame the club members for thinking that the boys were afraid. "Probably they lost most of their flock and they can't take chances," was what one member said and what others thought.

The boys watched the papers to see who had won the futurity. Ross again.

Next Friday they took their pigeons to the club rooms to enter them with all the rest for the 150-mile fly, the last race of the season and the longest. The birds that returned quickly would be used next season to be the fathers and mothers of young fliers, while all of the birds would be flown in the old bird races after they were through raising squabs.

As they entered the club rooms the few early

members who had gathered came forward to meet them and to congratulate them.

One said, "You didn't have to feel ashamed of that record. But we did hope you would compete in the futurity." That made them feel good.

Another asked them how many of their thirty-one they had lost, and when they answered, "Four," many men showed their astonishment, for some of the members had lost very heavily. Now there was nothing but seriousness when Pigeon City was mentioned —except, that is, for the broad smile on the face of the one member who had believed in them.

They entered their twenty-seven homers. The secretary was inclined to be more cordial now. Then they took their clock and went home. And after they were gone, there was again much discussion. Some of the members were inclined to believe they had a very good chance of winning. All of the members were surprised that they had entered the 150-mile race, and some frankly didn't know what to think. But even the most skeptical believed that Pigeon City homers were to be considered carefully in predicting the winner of the race.

On the way home the boys discussed the

chances of the various birds. The immigrants, as they called the newcomers, were a more or less unknown quantity, but they had done very well in the other race. Bud was extolling the wonders of Whitie, Bill was still rooting for Grizzle, and Dick didn't know what to think but he hoped that Blackie would win.

"I believe," said Bud, "that Grizzle would have done much better in clear weather. Even though he was not in the first five, he wasn't far behind, and I think he has as good a chance as any." They hadn't thought about the effect of the weather on him.

"That may be right, but how about a bird that can come home quickly through bad weather? He will do even better in clear," said Bill. Another thought to ponder.

"And," put in Dick, "I can't get that big red-check out of my mind. He is lazy, plain lazy, but he sure can fly. He has the biggest wing-spread of all the birds we own, but did you ever see him when he alights on the house?"

"Righto," said Bill, "he is nearly always the last one in, unless he is hungry."

"And he is the worst bully in the loft. He is bigger and knows his strength," added Bud. "All the rest are afraid of him."

"I wish there were some way of curing his

laziness. If we could do that, I'll bet he would be our best bird," said Dick, his champion. "We might see how he acts if he is hungry. Let him be shipped without having had a meal for a day. I'll bet he'd make for home and get inside the trap in jig-time."

"Let's try that some time after this race and see," said Bill.

Speculation as to the winner was not much use when there were so many extra-fine homers. They got home and went to bed.

Saturday dawned clear and cool. The secretary reported to the boys that the birds were on their way, in clear weather, which would surely last until they got home.

Again the birds had been liberated at seven sharp. There was little chance of any bird's getting home before nine, but at half-past eight Bud and Dick were on the roof watching. A gentle west wind was blowing, and they sat behind a broad chimney to keep warm, peering intently toward the southwest.

Shortly before nine a speck appeared so far away that it was barely visible. It grew more and more distinct. Then to the right of it another appeared. The first one to be seen came closer and closer. The one to the right seemed to be leading now. Closer they came and closer. The first one did not seem to be heading exactly toward them, but it was still far away. The other one was coming on the right course. Closer and closer. The one on the right was flying slightly lower now, the other was staying up. Closer and closer, and now they were almost home. No! only one was almost home; the one on the left was staying up. He went over, far up. The other drew in his wings and dropped, dropped, dropped. Zip, he went past them, a streak of blue, now a quick circle, and another and he was alighting on Pigeon City. Without a second's pause, he dashed through the trap.

Nor did the boy inside pause, either. In an instant he had caught him and slipped the band in the clock, and the first bird was timed.

While up on the roof two boys were smiling so broadly it seemed as though their faces would crack. "Grizzle!" both were saying over and over. "But it's going to be close. That one that went over has a time allowance. If he delays just a little getting in, we will beat *him* at least."

Five minutes passed. The red-check flashed by them and alighted, then leisurely looked about, slowly walked toward the trap, and went in.

"Wait a second," called a voice over the top of the roof. Bill heard. He knew that other birds were near. A German bird landed, then Blackie, then a Belgian. They, too, were recorded and the slide was closed. Bill looked out toward the roof. He whistled, and when he saw a face look over the edge he put his hand to his ear, meaning "What news?"

"More coming," yelled Bud, "but we can't clock them all. A lot just went over to some other lofts, but they were far behind ours that just landed. We'll be right down."

Dick, who was having such thrills watching the birds return, was loth to go, but he did drag himself away.

Fifteen more minutes passed. Ten more birds went through the trap. "Listen, fellows," said Bill. "Let's take the bands off all we have in and"—as he heard birds on the roof—"off those two that just came, and take them to the club to show that we have some homing pigeons." The two newcomers on the roof went through the wires and their bands too, were removed. The three boys ran to the house.

"Take us to the club, will you, Dad?" begged Bud. "We want to show that smart-aleck bunch how many birds we have home already so they will believe us." In a few minutes they were uptown at the club rooms.

Rushing in, Bud put the clock on the table.

"There are four bands in it. See, Mr. Jones. And just for good measure, here are twelve more," he said, and slapped them down before the astonished eyes of Mr. Jones. "Look at your watch and write down the time."

"Nine-thirty-three. Huh!" said Mr. Jones as he scratched the figure on a sheet of paper.

"After it you can write sixteen, for that's how many birds had reached home when we left."

"Say, Mr. Pigeon City," said Mr. Jones, putting out his hand, "we haven't done you boys justice. Let me shake your hand. I wouldn't wonder if you had some good pigeons after all."

"Do you really think so?" asked Bud, and he blushed. "Thanks very much. I'm glad you like them. We do too. Good-by."

And the club saw no more of Pigeon City birds or proprietors for a long while.

But by six o'clock that night all of the clocks were turned in, and the experts had begun to figure, making the time allowances and calculating carefully the speed in yards per minute.

Eager faces bent over the table. The final calculations were almost ready.

"Mighty close between the kids and Ross for first, wasn't it?" said an interested member. "But the kids put one over on us. Just fools' luck! They'll probably never win another race in their lives."

"Yes, but they have disgraced us for third place," put in another. "There they had three bands in the second clock, and so far all three are ahead of anybody for third, fourth and fifth."

"Boys, you haven't seen anything yet!" said the secretary. "I've got a surprise for you when this figuring is done." That made them all curious.

The calculations were finally completed, leaving the original results unchanged.

"Now tell me honestly, every one of you," asked the secretary, "how many birds did you have home by half-past nine?"

"Three," said one member.

"Five," said another.

"Six," said another.

"Anybody have more than six?" asked the secretary.

There was no answer. "Then," said the secretary, "look here and look closely." His hand was clenched about something. The members leaned over the big table to see the surprise. Slam, went his hand on the table. "Count 'em, darn it!" Then a pause while they counted the little bands.

"Sixteen, aren't there?" "There are," said Mr. Jones. "Well, those are what those kids brought in here at nine-thirty-three. Now what have we got to say?"

"All I can say," responded one elderly member, "is that maybe we haven't been giving those boys the credit that's due them."

"Well, well," exclaimed the secretary, "that's exactly what I told them myself."

Chapter XV

GLOOM COMES TO THE PARTNERS

In the early fall the partitions were put up in Pigeon City, and the cock birds and hens separated into different rooms. The immigrants had made much progress in increasing the number of birds in the loft, but these were separated with the rest. It was easy to distinguish them by their bands and the numbers on them.

Fall passed. Then a great grief entered the lives of the boys. Dear old Gramp, who had been getting weaker, died, and with his death there passed out of the lives of the boys a great friend. He had been almost one of them; he had given them counsel, had gone with them on their trips to look at and to buy pigeons, had practically started them in the pigeon game; Gramp, whom each boy thought of as his own grandfather, would never cease to be a happy memory throughout their lives.

Then winter came, and slowly dragged along, while the boys went coasting in the park, competed in their athletic sports at high school, and worked hard at their studies. And slowly the time for the remating of the pigeons approached.

Once in a while a calamity happens in the very best-regulated cities. Typhoid fever, or smallpox, or diphtheria may break out and it is often a considerable time before conditions right themselves. No disease came to the birds of Pigeon City, but something worse. There were really several calamities which grew out of the first great one.

Mr. Brighton and Mr. Hitchcock were good friends, both having been Yale graduates. That was what started all the trouble. Let us listen in on a conversation that took place in Mr. Brighton's home just at the time when the boys were making plans for spring mating.

"Paul," said Mr. Brighton to Mr. Hitchcock, "I have had an opportunity, as you know, to estimate on the building of a dam in Pennsylvania. It is to be for a dual purpose, serving both as a reservoir and as a power plant. I can take care of the job with the exception of the electrical end, and that is your field. How about going down there with me and estimating on the electrical equipment? Then if we get the job, you will install it. A reasonable bid will win the contract for me, and I will either sublet the electrical work to you or I will put you in charge and handle the whole thing myself."

"Sounds mighty interesting, Bill, old man. There's nothing I would like better. When shall we be off?"

"Well, as a matter of fact, the sooner the better. How soon could you get ready?"

"If necessary I can be ready in an hour, but I suppose you mean to start to-morrow?"

"Let's start to-night, Paul—that is, if it will not work any hardship on you."

"None in the least, I will phone my foreman and my secretary and I'll be here with my bag packed and ready in an hour. Will you phone for reservations?"

Two days later they returned, and two weeks after that Mr. Brighton walked through the hole in the fence to pay an informal call on his friend. "Paul, we have been awarded both contracts," he said. "This is an informal way to call, but we'll be on very informal terms for a while, so I'm breaking the ice."

The men shook hands as a symbol of satisfaction and gratitude. Both were necessary to the successful completion of the great task of building the dam. Mrs. Hitchcock came into the room where the men were talking. "Emily, could you pull yourself away from our home for a year or perhaps more? We have been awarded the dam job and the power-house installation."

"Of course, Paul, I'll go anywhere that your work calls you. But I will let you break it to George. Only just an hour ago all three boys were sitting in this very room discussing plans for raising more pigeons to win more races. It will be an awful shock to them."

"Yes, I know it will, but they are brave, and anyway there will be Dick to look after the pigeons after Bill and George are gone with us. I will fix it with our boy, and Bill, you can fix it with your son."

It wasn't so easy a matter to arrange as it looked. The boys had made such elaborate plans that it would be a wrench to leave. But leave they must, for both the families were to be taken to Pennsylvania while their fathers began and completed a great project that would stand as a monument to the abilities of both. After much persuasion the boys made up their minds that there was only one thing to do, and they agreed cheerfully.

That in itself would not have been a calamity. The three boys had adjusted themselves to the fact that Dick could look after the pigeons and train them to the best of his ability, or just work to increase the number. Out of a clear sky dropped the finishing blow. Mr.

Crampton came home late one afternoon with what was to him joyful news. Gleefully he announced it to his family while they were having supper. All but two of the children were now married. Dick was the youngest child and his sister was three years older. That was just right for Mr. Crampton's plans.

"To-day," he announced proudly, "the president called me to his office and told me of a bad tangle that has arisen in England. Our representative has got the company into some difficulties. The president has delegated me to go abroad and straighten the thing out, if it can be done. But it will be at least a year before everything is fixed. Mother, your expenses are to be paid as well as mine. Now I have decided, if you are willing, to take the children too. They are just the right age to learn a lot and I'm sure it will do them a great deal of good."

"Oh, Father, you don't mean it!" exulted Betty. "Are we to go abroad? Oh, that's the most wonderful thing!"

"I am simply delighted, Wilbur," said his wife. "You know I have always wanted to see England. This will be a great opportunity."

Not a sound from Dick.

"Why, Richard, what's the matter with

you?" said his mother. "Are you too happy for words?" Then a pause. "Oh, I see—it's the pigeons."

"Sure it is," he slowly responded. "Who is going to take care of them? Both of the other boys have to go away too. And just when we have the best flock in Greater New York, then you take me away, and we shall have to sell the whole lot. Nope—leave me out. I'd rather stay home and fly the pigeons than go to see a million Englands. Nothing doing." But well he knew that his talking would be of no avail.

Three of the glummest boys in the world sulked around for a week. What could they do? Nothing but sell the birds. Oh, if Gramp were only alive! Dear old Gramp. He would take the right kind of care of them.

One day as they were all in the coop talking over the matter further, the cheery voice of Miss Mary called in through the door which she had pushed ajar. "May I come in?"

" 'Course you may, any time, Miss Mary. You're always welcome."

"What's the matter, boys? They tell me you are thinking of selling these wonderful birds that won races for you. That isn't so, is it?"

"Well, goodness knows we don't *want* to!" said Bill. "But what can we do? Bud and I are going to Pennsylvania, and Dick has got to go to England. We can't let the pigeons starve!"

"But, boys, I am rather hurt, and so is my sister, that you haven't come to us to ask our help. You know we love the pigeons. Why, the beautiful creatures! It is one of our greatest joys to watch them from the window, or to come out in the yard in the summer. I could just spend the day watching them, the lovely hues on their necks and the colors of their feathers fascinate me so. Why not let *us* look after them for a year until you come back?"

The boys smiled for the first time in a week.

"We will feed them just as you say, and we'll water them and take good care of them for you. We should really love to do it. Don't sell the lovely creatures, please."

At last a solution was found.

"Well, you *are* awfully kind," said Dick. "It'll be great if you will do it. We had just about decided to give up racing them for this next year and concentrate on breeding a lot, maybe a hundred, to take out and train the following year when we shall all be back."

"That would be easy," said Miss Mary. "Of course we couldn't train them, but we could take care of them and see that they raised a lot of dear little squabs. You boys think it over and let us know." Then Miss Mary went home.

There was nothing else to do.

Chapter XVI

THE PIGEON MELTING-POT

UNDER the painstaking hands of the sisters the homers of Pigeon City prospered. The house was kept as clean as wax, and the birds were fed and watered with such regularity that no pigeons could have helped thriving. In a month the partitions were to be removed and the birds allowed to mate and rear their young. No more were to be allowed out of the house until the young birds came, and they were to be put into the fliers' room and the trap left open. Such were the directions that the boys left.

"Mary," said Ethel, one day, "since we are taking care of these birds, I should think we might be permitted to have a few of our own. Surely there is plenty of room just going begging."

"I'm sure no one would object," said her sister.

"Well, yesterday I saw the most beautiful bird in the pet-shop window. Oh, it was simply exquisite! Nearly all red except for some white feathers here and there. I do believe I shall buy it."

That very morning she did buy it, and two more also that took her eye. Two were what is known as flights and one was the mongrel of gorgeous hue. They were let out with the rest of the birds in Pigeon City.

A week more passed. "Ethel, look what I have found," called sister Mary. "Come—oh, you will love it! The cat was just going to kill it, and I took it away. Its wing seems to be hurt and it is bleeding." In her hands she held a common church-steeple pigeon. She put it in a box by the stove, washed its wounds, and fed it some warm milk and grain.

In a few days it was well, and of course, being such a pet it was put out in Pigeon City with the rest of their other pets and homers.

The time came when the partitions were taken down and the males and females mingled together and chose their mates. They also chose their homes, and went to work nesting. And the good sisters cared for them faithfully, occasionally buying a pigeon that pleased their fancy. Now and then when a stray dropped in, it was treated with every consideration. It seemed indeed that those that they brought in, and the strays, being weaker than the rest, got the better care. The greater part of their love and devotion was given to these, while the stronger homers because of their vigor were allowed to care for themselves.

They knew how the boys mated their pigeons by putting them together in the little cages in the grain room, and so they were careful to see that the old red-check was given one of these weaker birds for his mate so that she should be well cared for and protected. And Grizzle, whom they knew well and deemed strong, was mated with a flight, because they were especially fond of this particular one, and Grizzle could look after her and himself very well. They had a home on First Avenue, and they raised many squabs.

And then there was Whitie. They knew her too, and Blackie. To Whitie they mated the beautiful flight with the luscious green and gold neck. Mated to this almost-white bird it was quite a contrast, and they admired the handsome team. And Blackie, because of her great reputation, was mated with the church-steeple pigeon that Miss Mary had rescued from the cat. And so it went. A few of the homers were of course mated to homers. On the whole, the sisters were very happy at the wonderful progress they were making in raising squabs.

How could the boys be anything but gratified when they returned?

Day after day, never missing a feeding, the Gardner sisters worked ungrudgingly for the love of it; nobody could have attended better to the task of raising pigeons. Summer went by and fall came. They had now become very well acquainted with the pigeons, and knew them almost as well as the boys had known them. But now instead of forty-one they had in all a hundred and twenty-five. Then they closed up the nest-boxes and the year of breeding was over. A great flock of young birds passed out of the trap each morning and flew about and returned when they were ready.

Every month the boys sent their contribution of money for the feed, and everything went smoothly. Or at least, so the Misses Gardner thought.

Winter was half over. January had come. The dam was finished, and the Brighton and Hitchcock families returned to Brooklyn. They came home together. Nothing in the houses interested either of the two eager boys. Right to Pigeon City they ran. Miss Mary was there in her old dress cleaning the floor. The old loft looked even neater than usual to

the boys. It had even been recently white-
washed.

What a lot of birds!

"Oh, Miss Mary, how can we ever thank
you enough?" exclaimed Bill.

"Yes," Bud added. "This is wonderful,
better than we expected."

"Look at the young birds we have raised,"
said Miss Mary, pointing to the fliers' cage.
They looked. It was filled to overflowing.
All were properly banded, every one. Then
they looked over the old birds. There was old
Grizzle, and Whitie, and the little German
hen, and Blackie, and all the old familiar
feathered forms, just as distinct to the boys as
if they were so many people.

They moved about so happily that the birds
were constantly stirred up. But the boys had
seen the birds and knew they were well and
that they had multiplied, so they were very
happy.

"Miss Mary," asked Bud, as his eye fell on
an unfamiliar red mongrel pigeon with spots
of white splashed on its side, "what is that
funny-looking bird?"

"And what is that skinny black one there on
the top perch?" asked Bill.

"And there is a common pigeon, too.
Where did that come from?" asked Bud.

"And there is another one of those that look like flights! What is it?" Their eyes wandered about and they saw a lot of strange sights.

"Oh," said Miss Mary, "those are a few pets of Miss Ethel's and mine. You don't mind our having kept them here, do you, boys?"

"Why, of course not, Miss Mary. You have certainly been mighty kind to us. Now you won't have to work any more out here. We're home. We will take care of them from now on," said Bill.

"Just once in a while I would love to come out and look at our special pigeons and sweep up and do some little things around," said Miss Mary. "You won't mind, will you?"

"Of course not. Come as often as you want. And thanks more than we can say." Then they went indoors to put on their old clothes so they could come out and observe further.

In due course of time they had "observed" plenty! In a few days Dick came home and he helped them to "observe" some more. And what they saw did not please them.

There was Grizzle sitting right next to that miserable flight. There was the big red-check staying with another more miserable-looking mongrel. And dear Whitie had another flight for a mate! Blackie, of all things, was mated to nothing more than that poor, miserable, good-for-nothing common pigeon. And other wonderful birds had mates that were not the kind they should have had, at all!

"'None but the best for Pigeon City!'" almost wept Bill. "Can it be, fellows, that they have been mated to these mutts all summer and have wasted their fine heritage? Can it be that we shall have no young birds from these great pigeons to fly for Pigeon City? Oh, no—it can't be."

"Well, it surely looks that way," said Bud. "Only don't ask me to question Miss Mary about it. We owe both her and Miss Ethel too much to find fault. But gosh, fellows, I could bawl, because I'm afraid that it will be another year before we can race young birds from Pigeon City."

"Aw," said Dick, "let's cheer up. It could be worse." But tears were in his eyes as he said it.

Chapter XVII

THE SHEEP AND THE GOATS
ARE PARTED

IF Gramp had been alive he would have been talking about the pigeons he had when he was a boy, and what he did with them. That is the way with old age. Life often hasn't the zest it should have because of the constant turning-back, with all too little room for looking ahead. But instead of turning back, Bud and Dick and Bill had only a rosy glow of memory, a haze of happiness behind, and the future ahead. They lived, to be sure, in the present, but in their thoughts they were most often in the future. So the results of the calamity which had befallen Pigeon City seemed less serious because to them the past was not important except for the lessons it had taught. Here it was the middle of winter. Soon it would be time to mate the homers, and then would come the excitement of seeing the squabs develop and begin to fly. This would be followed by the training and the races, and all that went with them.

At once the partitions were put in place, making four separate rooms. The cock birds were put in one, in another the hens, and in the flying room the birds belonging to the Gardner sisters, so that they might fly out and possibly get lost some day. Miss Mary and Miss Ethel thought that putting their birds together was very nice indeed!

As the boys watched the last year's birds they could readily see that some of them gave evidences of a lack of breeding. There was a mongrel look that was anything but "exclusive." The power of the homer was lacking. But the question was, would they become worthy fliers because at least one parent had been good? Time would tell. It would be worth while to keep them just for the experiment.

Then there were others that certainly looked for all the world like real homers, but once in a while the boys just faintly thought they could detect a shade, if only faint, of something wrong.

"Well, you can't tell by the looks of a frog how far he can jump," said Dick, "and perhaps some of these that look perfectly good will prove to be mongrels even though they do look like homers."

"Yes," added Bud, "and who knows but that those half-breed flights will make good homers? Maybe they will have the looks of flights and the homing qualities of homers."

So guesses and ideas were plentiful, but they could not prove anything; it would take more than that.

It was nearly time to mate the birds. The old birds were well known to the boys. But last year's birds were strangers. One day when they were wondering just what to do, a thought occurred to Bud. "What do you say if we put all the last year's birds into the fliers' cage and get them flying well, and then take them on a few training flies on some of the warm days? They are old enough, and perhaps we can get rid of the mongrels that way. It would be painless!"

"Oh," said Dick, "but what about the Gardner pigeons? We can't take them away. And we oughtn't to let ours fly with the others. The flights will keep the homers from flying off on scouting trips. Flights fly in little circles up overhead, and that will spoil the homers."

"Righto," said Bill, "and what about the flight breeding that a lot of our young birds carry? Won't that make them fly in small circles just as if the flights were actually in the flock? Let's ask Miss Mary whether she minds if we train her birds too."

All three descended upon the sisters.

"Miss Mary, Miss Ethel," said Bill, "we want to do a little training. Don't you want to help us?"

"Why, how thrilling!" said Miss Mary. "Yes, indeed. How can we help?"

"Well," said Bill, "we want to take your birds and put them in the little coop in Dick's yard. You see, we are afraid that the flights will keep the flock from going out if they all fly together. It is quite important that they fly wide and not just in little circles. Do you mind?"

Miss Ethel didn't like the idea at all. "Boys, I might say that I for one do mind. I have got the pigeons so tame that they fly right there to the window-sill and eat out of my hand."

"But," answered Bill, "here's another thought. Suppose that we do train them; I am afraid that if we took yours away they would get lost and would never return."

"Why, the idea!—to suggest that your pigeons are better than ours! We have no intention of losing them, and I for one don't believe that you could lose them any more quickly than you can lose your own," said Ethel.

Things were breaking just exactly as the boys had hoped. They had awakened a little sporting spirit in Miss Ethel, at least.

Now Bud spoke, "Well, I'll make a bet with you, and I don't usually bet either. I'll bet you that not one of your pigeons can find its way home from across the Hudson River, and that some of ours can. And here's what I'll do. If any of yours come home, we will feed them for a whole year for nothing. If they do not come home you will be out only the pigeons. Is it a go?"

"Why, Ethel," interrupted Mary, "that is a splendid idea. We shall have no feed bills for a year. I'm willing. Are you?"

Ethel was skeptical. "How could those beautiful things that love this home so much fail to come?" she said. "Haven't we loved them and treated them with the greatest care all this time? They know their home much better than the others. But I should dislike losing even one. I don't believe I care to risk it."

"Oh, be a sport, Ethel," urged Mary. "I'm willing. Why aren't you?"

"Well," finally agreed Ethel, "if you think I would not be a sport if I refused, I'll agree;

but I warn you, you will see our pigeons all home first because they have come to love us so much. I know they will beat those old bullies that won't ever give them any peace!"

Having obtained consent, the boys knew very well that Pigeon City would soon be rid of a few undesirables; but how many of the mongrels they could not guess.

For two weeks the birds had regular flies every morning and afternoon. One thing was very certain: the flights among them, and the flight breeding in some of them, made the flock act very differently from the old flock of pure homers. Instead of the great sweeping circles, the flock now flew in short, choppy circles. They would not take the scouting flies, nor did they seem to get the great pleasure from the flies that the pure homers obtained. But this condition was soon to pass, the boys felt.

When the appointed Saturday arrived, the boys boxed up the many birds with the help of the sisters, who wept over theirs as they kissed them and bade them farewell. It was quite a load that each boy carried as the three boarded a trolley-car and rode out to the very limits of the city, on Long Island. In all they had ridden about ten miles. The birds that returned from this fly were to be taken the next week across the Hudson River.

At the end of the line they got out. Not far away was an open lot of considerable size bordered by houses, newly erected or in the process of construction. They went out to the middle, cut the strings, and liberated the birds. They rose in a flock. Now they were up

Map of
NEW YORK CITY
AND VICINITY

NEW JERSEY
THE PALISADES
Bronx
LONG ISLAND SOUND
NASSAU
LONG
ISLAND
Newark
Jersey City
FLUSHING
Queens
PIGEON CITY
Jamaica
Bayonne
Brooklyn
Richmond
STATEN ISLAND
JOHN ST.
ROCKAWAY
NEW BRUNSWICK
SANDY HOOK
ATLANTIC OCEAN

above the housetops, now higher and still higher.

Over to one side a large flock of flights was making its picayune circles.

By the time the birds were at an altitude of three or four hundred feet and the boys expected they would bear toward home, a curious thing happened. Something seemed to explode the flock. Instead of staying together they suddenly began to fly in every direction, scattering to the four winds. Some moved in circles toward home, some in the very opposite direction, and some made wider and wider circles. This was new.

The boys stood watching the birds, then looked at each other. For fifteen minutes there were birds from Pigeon City to be seen here and there, for a very large flock had been liberated. Three birds stayed together, flying centrally in typical flight circles. Then slowly they moved toward the large flock of flights, which was still up, urged by the owner who whistled and threw gravel at them when they tried to alight. Before many minutes had passed the three had swung in unison with the rest and were swallowed up. Immediately the owner stopped exciting the flock and they settled on his roof. And thus three flights that had done much to damage the heritage of the homers of Pigeon City were finally eliminated.

Now and again a pigeon would dart here and there rather wildly excited, it seemed to the boys, but they had seen enough and, taking the trolley, they went home.

When they walked through Bud's house to Pigeon City, there were the sisters sitting waiting for their dear pigeons. In the fliers' room were a flock of fifty or more pert, powerful-looking homers, some on perches, others calmly eating, but all with that look of ability which, to the experienced eye of the pigeon fancier, distinguishes the real homer from the common pigeon.

"Well, who won the bet?" asked Bill, the only one who dared to speak.

Miss Mary smiled, rather pathetically. Miss Ethel looked away. There was nothing to be said. They both went into the house.

"Let's check them up, boys, and record their numbers. Those birds are the homers," said Bud. "The mongrels and any poor homers are lost. A few more may still come back, but this is the cream. This is 'Pigeon City class.' *None but the best for Pigeon City!* We are not out of the running, you bet."

"Nope. What's the use? Wait till next week if it's warm and that will tell us more," said Dick. So they waited.

For three days afterwards pigeons kept straggling into Pigeon City. Were these the pure homers, or were they mongrels, and were their homer parents then exerting a strong enough influence to help them along more than if they had had no homer breeding in them at all?

The next Saturday was bitter cold. The next was snowy. The third was warm enough and fine, just right for a pigeon race.

On the way over on the ferry from Bay Ridge to Staten Island there was further speculation. One great difficulty had arisen. How were the boys going to make it right with the Misses Gardner for losing their pigeons, after all the trouble they had taken, and after all these years when there had been no objection to the fly across the back of their yard? Since their birds were gone they had taken no further interest in the pigeons. What could be done to bring back their coöperation? None of the boys knew.

As soon as the boat docked, the great flock of homers and part-homers flew up from the upper deck, much to the amusement of a few of the passengers who had remained to see them go. On the whole the birds behaved quite well, but a few acted wildly as on the previous fly three weeks before.

It was a good test and also a good way of ridding Pigeon City of inferior stock, for only the real homers returned and a few others straggled in during the week. If only they had all come the first day, that would have simplified things greatly. It was these late arrivals that worried the boys. Should they use them to breed from, or should they sell them and use only the early arrivals? No, it was decided to take the whole lot seventy-five miles away and use only those that returned from there. That would tell the tale. There

were plenty of birds to take chances with.
There would still be sufficient stock to raise
squabs for them, and there were the old birds
too.   After all it seemed that this would be
the best way out.   So they waited for a warm
week-end.

Chapter XVIII

FRIENDS AGAIN

What worried the boys was the loss of the Misses Gardner's friendship. Worry takes a lot of the joy out of life. So after worrying and wondering they decided upon a plan to win back the sisters' affection.

"Won't you both come out to Pigeon City and see the birds?" asked Bill who was the official delegate to propose the meeting. "We want you both to be as much interested as you were."

The sisters smiled because they knew the boys really liked them, and acquiesced. Throwing some wraps about their shoulders they were quickly in the loft talking with the boys and admiring the beautiful birds.

"We are awfully sorry that we lost all of your pigeons," said Bill. "We want to make it right with you and we don't know how to do it. Would you be willing to accept some of our best homers to make up for the loss of the others?"

"Why, you dear boys!" exclaimed Miss

Mary. "You don't need to feel that you have lost them for us. You knew more about pigeons than we did, and we have learned that a homer has a certain mental ability that other pigeons lack, whatever it is, that helps him to get home. You don't need to give us any pigeons. But we shall be happy if you will invite us often to look at them."

"But we really *want* you to have some. And you know you don't need an invitation to come out here. Come as often as you like."

"Yes," added Dick. "The next warm Saturday we are going to have another training fly, and the birds that get home will be the ones we shall use for raising the squabs next season. Won't you come out and watch the birds return? It is really very exciting. You can sit right in the loft and see them, or if you choose you can dress up warmly and go up on the roof with us and see them coming in from the distance, for that is the most exciting time of all."

"That's right," urged Bill, "and if you had a few pigeons of your own you would get even more excitement wondering about them and seeing them come in over your head and drop down here at Pigeon City. The only thing is for you to have some of your own. Take your choice."

"But," said Miss Ethel, "I feel that somehow or other I wouldn't like this so much because I think it is cruel." She was thinking of the young ones that they had raised. "If the mothers and fathers of these young ones couldn't find their way home, how can we expect that their babies will? Think of how terrible it will be if you let them all go and the ones that can't get home will have to stay out and freeze. Oh, it's just unthinkable. That would be the worst cruelty imaginable."

The boys knew well that if a pigeon were lost he would soon find a loft to live in and would be treated very well in almost any of them, because they themselves had had many strange birds drop in to stay with them. No, they could not believe it was cruelty, and were about to explain when sister Mary said something to which, while they may have thought it without realizing, they had never given words.

"Ethel," she said, "I am beginning to see things in a very different light."

"Different light? How?" replied her sister.

"Well, homing pigeons are unlike all others. You don't doubt that, do you?"

"No, but what has that to do with cruelty?"

"Everything. We were trying to raise pigeons that we liked because they pleased our eyes; the boys are raising pigeons that are best suited to racing with all that is necessary for that. Those two things are very different."

"Very," said Miss Ethel, "but we didn't know that when we allowed the breeds to mix. That wasn't our fault."

"But it was, Ethel. There is no excuse for ignorance. And now that I see things differently I realize that the cruelty of it came through our ignorance. If we hadn't allowed the breeds to mix there would be no need to lose more than a few pigeons. Now, all of the mixed breeds will probably be lost, just as some were when all of ours were lost. Isn't that right, boys?"

"But it isn't cruelty, Miss Mary," said Bill. "Even if pigeons are lost they find a home, maybe one they like better than this."

"No, but that isn't what Miss Mary means," said Bud. "She means that even if there were cruelty it could all have been avoided by mating only pure homers where there was homers' work to do. Don't you, Miss Mary?"

"Yes," she said, "that's exactly it."

"But if you wish, we could perhaps do away with all the cruelty that Miss Ethel is afraid of. We could sell all of the birds that required more than a day to return from the last training fly. How would that be?"

"Oh, no, that would be still more cruel," objected Ethel. "Somebody might eat them. They would have to be killed. I would prefer not to know what has become of them rather than to think that the poor things would be killed."

"Yes, and with us," said Dick, "we would be taking a chance that way. We might sell a bird that was pretty good. We would much rather take a chance and let them all out and see which ones come home."

"Well," said Miss Ethel, "I have already proved that I know nothing about pigeons, so you do as you think best."

"That's right, Ethel. These boys know what they are doing." Then turning to the boys, Miss Mary said, "How about the pigeons you want us to own? May we select them now?"

"Right now!" said Bill for the boys.

"How many shall we choose?"

"Six or eight. How many would you like?"

"Do we understand that you are going to take care of them? Will they be ours just for the pleasant part of the work, if there is any?" asked Miss Ethel.

"Gracious," said Bill, "that would be very little for us to do for you after all you did for us for a whole year! I'd say take a dozen if you want, and remember you know as much about the breeding of these birds as we do ourselves."

"Five will be enough. You choose first, Ethel."

"Better take at least three each," said Bud.

"All right. Shall I choose my three first? Very well. I would like that shiny black one up on the corner perch with the white feathers in his wings. And—"

Bill cut her off rather impolitely. "No, don't choose that one; he will never come back. He's a half-breed. Choose the plain ones that have colors to suit you. Now that blue-check looks good to me, for example."

"Ah, but I like mine to be distinctive."

"Well," said Dick, "here's what I should do. Let's take the record book and see which ones were more than a day getting home, and take them right out of the room for a while and then Miss Mary and Miss Ethel will have better chances of selecting birds that will make them proud."

This help pleased the sisters very much. When they had selected their pigeons, the boys found that Miss Ethel had chosen the ones with the most showy colors, while Miss Mary had gone to the very other extreme and had selected those with the drabbest colors of all, namely the only three black ones in the lot.

The great worry had now vanished.

Then when Saturday came and the weather was warm they drew lots; and Dick, having lost, was despatched with the birds. All three took the boxes to the train and placed them in the baggage car. Then Bud and Bill returned to Pigeon City.

The Misses Gardner were thrilled to see the birds return, and they argued with each other and the boys as to whose birds would win. They sat upon the roof, well blanketed, and watched with great excitement as one of Miss Ethel's birds, with white feathers in its wings, was among the first to arrive, closely followed by two of Miss Mary's blacks.

But that single fly rid Pigeon City forever of the bad stock that had been planted with the good by the well-meaning but poorly directed intentions of their kind neighbors. Now the breeding work could proceed.

Chapter XIX

THE OLD BIRDS RACE

THE purity of the breed was now established by test. Now came the problem of mating. First they considered the old birds. Which should they mate together? The very first selection was to find the proper partner for Grizzle. The black hen was chosen for him. Then came the red-check, for he too was a star even though he was lazy. He was paired off with Whitie because Whitie had pep, and this combination might produce squabs having both energy and racing ability. These were the two pair they considered most likely to produce their future winners.

There were also the German hen and the Belgian blue cock, which they mated because they both promised very well. The rest were allowed to choose their own mates. Thus the breeding season was in full swing. Now there would be many youngsters, each of which would give the members of the club something to think about. But also there would be more weight for the boys to carry on their training flies. To that end they built three neat carrying cages on the order of suitcases, with partitions, each little compartment accommodating four birds. Each case had six of these compartments. Thus in the three, seventy-two birds could be carried at one time. All these preliminary arrangements were ready before the training season began.

From the old and the new birds it would take but a short time to raise one hundred squabs, and they decided that after this was done they would begin to fly the old birds and thus prepare them for the old bird races.

With so much to do the spring went by quickly and summer was upon them, and the time for the races was approaching. The loft was filled with great homers, the best to be found. A huge flock of powerful-winged fliers rose above Pigeon City to circle a while or go on scouting flies.

Now it became necessary to cut another hole in the roof and place a trap for the old birds, and then they too were given opportunities to fly, as well as to raise squabs.

Training the old birds was done by shipping directly with the club birds in order to avoid additional expense. Three-quarters of the lot were shipped each time. Care was necessary in selecting the proper ones to ship because some had small squabs to feed, and in that case only one of a pair was sent; others were not in their best condition. But each time three-quarters of the old birds were shipped. There was first a 100-mile training fly, during which just two birds were lost; then another over the northerly course in which one bird was lost, perhaps killed by a hawk; no one will ever know. Then came the 150-mile race.

As usual, the birds were banded and shipped, and in due time liberated. The results showed that the winner was none other than Grizzle, while the bird that was second was a big black owned by Miss Mary. Then the birds of two other club members followed. That was a great start. But the race in two weeks would be harder. It was to be two hundred and fifty miles. In this the greatest homers were all entered. Again it was won by the boys, who got both first and second. First came old Red-Check, second came Grizzle, but he was found to have a pair of small pinion feathers broken in one wing, which perhaps accounted for the loss of time.

With these two races over, and very few Pigeon City fliers lost, the great test of the whole career of Pigeon City drew near, the 500-mile race. In one sense the flock had become too cumbersome; there were several more old birds than were actually needed, so it looked as if this great fly would accomplish some weeding. Every possible bird was shipped. They were two days on the train; another day of poor weather delayed the start; and then came word by telegraph that they were in the air at five o'clock in the morning. It had been expected that they would start on Friday, but it was now Saturday and the boys were home and waiting anxiously. Which one would be the first of sixty great birds to arrive? All the other club members were on the *qui vive*. So were the Misses Gardner.

The boys figured it out on a mile-a-minute basis. Between eight and nine hours for the five hundred miles would be taken if they made that speed.

As soon as they were liberated, the birds rose to a fair height, a whole swarm in all. In a few minutes, wherever the station agent looked he could see homing pigeons. Salisbury, North Carolina, had never seen so many pigeons before. For nearly half an hour some of them circled, but others wasted no time and broke away from the rest and headed northeast, toward home. If you could have followed them you would have seen among this first group a big black flier, a leisurely red-

Wherever the station agent looked he could see
homing pigeons

check, a smaller black bird, an almost white
one, and a grizzle-colored, to say nothing of
fifty or more pigeons of all colors and sizes.
You would scarcely call it a flock, since each
bird was a long distance from every other, but
all were going in the same direction as if anxious to reach the same destination.

Now they had passed Greensboro, long before most people were out of bed. Soon South
Boston was left behind, then Petersburg, Virginia. Now the birds were stringing out;
some had gained on the rest; some had flown
more to the east and some more to the west.
There were no landmarks to guide them, nothing but that instinct which has guided so many
thousand pigeons, and which would be passed
on to their descendants.

The morning was growing warmer, and the
birds flew higher where the air was cooler.
Now none was close enough to think of the
other. Did they know they were racing, or
was each bent only on getting to the home
that meant so much to him? As the day
wore on the birds could see a wide body of
water in the distance. Some flew to the left
trying to escape it, and lost time. A few
others ignored it, for there ahead was the shore
on the other side, quite visible to their far-

seeing eyes.   Straight as speeding arrows flew
these magnificent birds.   One was now far in
the lead; another, owing to his ability, though
far in the rear of these better leaders, was well
ahead of the general group.   It was Red-
Check.

By noon they were over Maryland, having
left Virginia behind.   By one o'clock Grizzle
crossed another wide body of water and was
now over southern New Jersey.   But other
fliers were close followers.   The big Belgian
cock was scarcely a mile behind, while the
German hen and Blackie were no more than
that, but over slightly to the west.   And still
further in the rear was Red-Check, making
good speed.   Now he was urged on by a different feeling from any he had ever before experienced in the air.   It was hunger.   There
was more than a desire to return home: he
wanted food, and water.   He was very thirsty.
There was only one place where he knew he
could get it.   So he added a little to his speed
and slowly began to gain on the rest.   Then
again he thought of his mate and their squabs,
not knowing that the mate was in the air with
him, also trying to get home.

In his endeavors he passed many of the club
birds that he could see on either side, usually

very far away. The birds on the left now began to observe familiar landmarks which gave them courage. Grizzle and several of the others were heading straight, thinking of nothing but home and mate, food and water.

By two o'clock southern New Jersey was left behind and there was now familiar country for all, to cheer them on. The day continued warm, but the birds far up almost to the scattering clouds did not mind it, for the rush of air passing their bodies, and the higher altitude, kept them comfortably cool. Now the distance between Grizzle and Red-Check was less than it had been by several miles. The great breast muscles of Red-Check drew the powerful wings with their wide expanse, faster and faster, while Grizzle was giving of his best every minute. Now in the distance was still another body of water, and there below and on the other side was Staten Island, so familiar to them all. They became more and more cheerful in their rush for home. Faster and faster flew the lazy red bird. Steadily flew Grizzle, but the distance between them was closed down to less than a mile. Only fifteen miles to fly, and while Grizzle was becoming tired, Red-Check was flying harder than ever.

Now he could see Grizzle ahead and recog-

nized him.   Soon Staten Island was passed
and the East River crossed, and in the distance
both birds could see the familiar smokestacks
and factory buildings of their home surroundings.   On they rushed far in the lead of all of
the other birds.

On the housetops the interested boys and
their friends watched, peering through the sun-
light that made it difficult for them to see.
And inside of Pigeon City a lad waited, alert
for the warning of feet upon the roof.   Suddenly, before he realized it, a pair of birds
whizzed by him and dropped down to Pigeon
City.   Bud, who was waiting, heard not one
pair of feet but two alight on the roof.   One
was rushing for the trap; one stood still for
a fraction of a second, as he had always done,
from habit.   Then he, too, walked through
the trap wires.

No more than seconds separated them; but
Grizzle—Grizzle was first, and Red-Check
was second, in one of the greatest races in
pigeon history.

Experience told Bud not to rush off to the
club rooms.   This time he waited, and before
long he had taken the bands from a dozen
birds, among which were Whitie, Blackie, Miss
Mary's black, and Miss Ethel's young bird

with the white feathers in its wings. Not until all of these had come in did Bud take the bands to the club rooms.

During that one day forty-three birds returned. These would be the parents of the coming generation.

Chapter XX

JEALOUSY IN THE CLUB—AND SOME
GOOD ADVICE

No prize is more coveted than the honor and the cup which come from winning the 500-mile race. It is easy to forgive the consternation of some of the old members of the club. Some rather bitter things were said. One veteran who had been flying homers for thirty years started the discussion, when he remarked to a group of club members: "I hear the kids won again, both first and second. Beginners' luck! Another year they won't be in the running. Watch them next week and see. I'll bet they don't come within the first fifty places at a thousand miles. In fact, I doubt if they have the courage to enter a bird."

"Now, look here," interrupted Mr. Ross, who had always been a friend to the boys, "I am willing to say one thing in favor of the young fellows: they have some great pigeons, and they know how to handle them. But we must remember that we shall soon see whether they really are as wise as their records lead us to believe. They began with the best stock there was. I know because I furnished some of it. Where the rest came from they won't tell. They had a good start, but now let's see what they can do when it comes to breeding their own."

"Yes," interrupted another, "I'll be surprised if they win a single young bird race."

"You fellows make me tired," said a large man who had always had pigeons among the best. "The real brains of that bunch is dead. When that old man died that was the end for the kids. He got them started and they relied on him. Just watch them from now on. How could three boys like that be expected to win races? It's the birds they started with that are doing all their winning."

"Well, we shall soon find out," said Mr. Ross.

There was much shaking of heads, much skepticism. One and all, with the exception of Mr. Ross, the club members were doubtful whether the boys could win any more races, and they didn't seem to care if they let the boys know their feelings in the matter.

There were two weeks between the 500-mile race and the 1000-mile in order to let the birds rest. On the week-end between, an im-

portant meeting was called at the club rooms,
which was attended not only by the great majority of the club members but by the Pigeon
City boys as well. The meeting was for the
purpose of determining whether the northern
or the southern course would be the more ad-
visable over which to fly the 1000-mile race.

Pigeon City had but one vote. The boys
had joined the club under that name instead
of joining separately. But they entered the
club rooms together.

"Hello," said a man nearest the door, in a
rather unfriendly tone of voice.

"Good evening," answered Bud in such a
cordial tone that the man felt embarrassed.

"I suppose Pigeon City is going to win the
1000-mile race in a walk?" asked another
man, irritatingly.

"Guess the birds will try; we've done our
part," answered Bill. "If we could only do
the flying I'm sure Pigeon City would win.
Anyway, we're counting on our birds to make
a respectable showing."

They took their seats. A man in the row
behind leaned forward and addressed the boys.
"Got any young birds worth flying?" he asked.

"Rather wait and see when the races come,"
answered Bud. "They'll be here soon

enough." That was just the sort of reply that exasperated the men more than any other he might have made.

The meeting was called to order. The usual business was transacted. Then came the matter of deciding upon the course. Various members expressed their opinions, and the sentiment seemed to be about equally divided. Some wanted to ship the birds to Canada, and some to the Southwest.

Up spoke a younger member, Bud. "If we want to make time," he said in a voice that tried to be grown up but which still had a boyish pitch, "we ought to ship them on the southern course. Nearly every one of our races has been from that direction."

"Yes," added a boy sitting next to him, "I believe that we should ship them south."

"Say," interrupted the chairman, "how many voices do you boys want? Only one of you is a member, or rather your Pigeon City is a member. You have only one vote and one opinion."

"Looks as if we weren't so very popular," whispered Dick to Bud. And from then on not a remark came from the proprietors of Pigeon City, but they cast their vote. The birds were flown on the northerly course.

When the boys were gone, one member said

to a group, "Now watch whether the boys win the race. I voted for the northerly course just to make sure they wouldn't win."

"Yes, it's a disgrace that we should all be beaten by a lot of youngsters like that," added another member. "I'm glad, too, that we have put them where they belong."

On the way home a fourth member had joined the three Pigeon City experts. It was Mr. Ross. They passed a few minutes in pleasant conversation, and then the subject turned to the attitude of the club members toward Pigeon City.

"Mr. Ross," said Dick, "will you tell us why those men dislike us so? We have always been polite and respectful, and I for one see no reason why they should be sore."

"I think I can explain that very easily, boys," he answered. "You must put yourselves in their places. To them you are a mystery. You appear out of nowhere, you come with birds they do not know, and begin to win races almost from the start. You keep aloof, you don't bet with them, and yet you win. Some of them have lost a lot of money because your birds have beaten theirs. You don't bet, and neither do I, but if I did I would bet on your birds. However, that is neither here nor there. If you want to get closer to them, let them beat you once in a while. You are young and have time ahead to win your races. Let them win for a change. Now, if I had your birds and won the races they would all feel pretty happy about it. I guess it must be the fact that you are so much younger and that you are newcomers."

"But how are we going to help it when the birds hurry home?" said Dick.

"Easy enough. Just don't put the bands from the first ones in the clocks. *You* will know the real winner and you will have the satisfaction of that. Well, here's where I get off. Good night." And Mr. Ross got out, leaving the boys to discuss his good advice.

They did discuss it thoroughly.

A few nights later, the three boys called on Mr. Ross. Bud asked him, "Mr. Ross, what is the rule about entering pigeons? Must a person enter his own or may he enter some other person's if he wants?"

"He may enter any bird he wants to as long as he brings it to the club, pays the entry fee, and enters it. But it wouldn't do him much good to enter another man's, because he couldn't get the band in the clock; the bird would not come to his loft but would go to its own home."

"Oh, yes, it would do him good," said Bud.

"If that is the rule, we have decided to take your advice, and we have an idea to propose. It won't do us any good to have the club members hate us. We have a few young birds that are wonders. One was bred from Grizzle and the black hen. We got from you the egg from which the black hen hatched. Then there are a few others that from present indications appear to be great fliers, and we think we still have a good chance of winning, or at least of being among the very first. You understand that we don't want to violate any rule but we do want the birds flown."

"Yes, but what is your idea?" said Mr. Ross.

"We would like you to let us have about six or eight birds to test out. We want to take them to our house and get them used to flying back to yours. When we have taken them a number of times and we are sure they will get home quickly, we shall be satisfied. Then what we shall do is this. Before every race we are going to bring our young birds over here to your home and let you take them to the club and enter them as your own. Then when they come home to us, we shall have some of your birds ready and we can take the bands off ours, put them on yours and let them go, and they will go to your house where you can put the bands in your clock. So you see we'll have a relay race."

"The idea is," said Bill, "we don't want to win any more for a time so as to see whether it makes for better feeling."

"Excellent idea! But really, boys, that is too good for me. I will win a few races for a change if you can make the transfer of the bands quickly enough. I'm willing to try. The only difficulty is that the secretary may recognize the band numbers as the ones he assigned to you; but that is very unlikely. Yes, I'll be happy to do that, and it will help you a lot. Then I understand that for the rest of the flying season, certain of your young birds are to be my property."

So it was agreed. The young birds that looked best would be entered by Mr. Ross. The 100-mile race would be held in three weeks. The next night the homers for the 1,000-mile old bird race would be entered and shipped. That would be the last fly of the season for the old ones.

One might expect that a 1,000-mile race would be very exciting, but the boys found it otherwise. There was too much anxiety connected with it; they wondered where the birds were staying overnight, what time the first flier would come in, which of many kinds of weather might beset their paths.

Instead of sending their best fliers, Pigeon City withheld all of their choicest and shipped the second choice of the old birds that were in condition. Thirty went away with the rest of the club birds and unfortunately only eighteen returned. On Sunday, two days after they had been liberated, a homer with white feathers in its wings appeared. On the afternoon of the same day two more came. Not for a week were all eighteen in, and the proprietors of Pigeon City made up their minds that the distance was not worth the honors it brought; the overnight hazards were too great, with weather and what-not to be considered. Henceforth they would fly their birds at distances from which they could reach home between daylight and dark. And they were very happy that they had not sent their favorites. But happiest was Miss Ethel, whose pigeon had done so well, although winning only third place in the race.

Now the club members knew they were right. The boys couldn't win the 1,000-mile race! It was beginners' luck that they had had. At once they felt a little better toward the boys. Mr. Ross' advice had been good.

Chapter XXI

MR. ROSS WINS EVERYTHING

It was time for the young bird races. The club rooms were abuzz with voices, the sound of hundreds of fine homers cooing, the flapping of the fighters' wings, the moving of crates by members, and the occasional calling of members' names by the secretary.

Pigeon City birds had been entered and the boys had gone home. Mr. Ross was at the table entering his birds.

"For goodness' sake, Ross, this is new for you! I thought you stuck to the old-time colors, but here's a grizzle." The bird was one of the sons of old Grizzle.

"I've changed my policy somewhat," said Mr. Ross. Then he announced to the club members, "This bird has been doing very well in the training flies, so if any of you want to bet, here is a good chance for first." Several members looked the pigeon over.

"Here's another likely one, too, this black fellow. I believe he is one of the best. But this red grizzle is the one I would bet on if I were a betting man." It was a son of old Red-Check and Whitie. He was a long, rangy bird, almost white, but splashed with red feathers, altogether handsome and with a head that looked keen. Mr. Ross exhibited him proudly to the club members. Then he finished entering his birds and went home.

During the summer the boys had made two improvements or additions to Pigeon City. First they had built a small hut on Bud's roof in which they could sit and be somewhat protected on chilly days. In this they had arranged a button, and from the housetop a wire led down to Pigeon City, where it was connected with a light and a battery. This was the signal to the boy in the house that birds were coming. He could then be ready, and there would be no further need for shouting, as had been necessary sometimes in the past. The noise had sometimes frightened the racers.

Miss Mary and Bill were sitting in this hut. In Pigeon City Bud and Dick waited.

The light flashed on. Bud reached for one of Mr. Ross' birds which was loose in the fliers' room. A big red grizzle bird came through the trap. Instantly the band was removed and put on Ross' bird, and Bud tossed it out of the door, and up it flew for its own home.

Then came two more birds; one of these, a grizzle, had his band removed and transferred to another of Ross' birds, and he too was relayed. Then some more came in, and finally the boys put a few bands in their clock and started both ends running by closing the slides. When they were ready they took it to the club rooms.

"Ha, ha!" said a particularly offensive person. "You aren't the first one here this time, I see. Perhaps you won't win this race!"

But another member cut him off by reminding him in a whisper that the boys were so sure of themselves that they were getting conceited.

As they were leaving, Mr. Ross came in, appearing very glum indeed. It was easy to see that something had gone wrong. But the boys went home without ascertaining the difficulty. When they reached home they were called to the telephone. It was Mr. Ross. "Boys, our plan didn't work. One of my birds will get second, I believe, but two of yours were way ahead. The trouble was that those pesky birds you let out came here and just sat on the roof and wouldn't come in. I was so mad I almost shot one. After they had sat there for some time along came one of my own birds and I clocked her and so we lost."

"I know what was the trouble," said Bud, "we let them eat too much. Next time let's not feed them, so they will hurry home for food and water."

Mr. Ross did get second. The boys did not so much as get fifth, although they knew well that they might have got first with their third bird home. This very knowledge made them feel as good as though they had actually received this coveted honor.

"But next week—oh, you club members, wait and see! A Pigeon City flier will be first, even though you don't know it," chorused the boys.

And when, next week, the results of the 100-mile futurity were announced, Mr. Ross had got first and second in one of the most

novel pigeon races of all time. The Pigeon
City boys had done their work admirably. A
bird darted through the wires of Mr. Ross'
trap and almost dove for the water trough.
Mr. Ross quickly snatched it up, to find not
one band on it, but two. The red grizzle and
the brown grizzle had come through the wires
of the Pigeon City trap together, and the boys
put both of their bands on one of Mr. Ross'
birds and let him start for home, hungry and
thirsty, so that Mr. Ross not only won the race
but received second as well.

Now the boys were highly elated, because
they realized that their birds that had so
closely followed the winners, and one of which
they clocked in time for it to get fourth, were
actually better than any others in the club.

The same plan was followed in the 150-mile
race with the same result, except that Pigeon
City won third.

And now the club members were becoming
more cordial, since others than the boys were
now winning. It was very clear to them that
Pigeon City's last year's results were nothing
more than beginners' luck.

And so another year had passed, a year
filled with happy memories of races won, of
glory achieved, and better still, of the satisfaction of knowing just among themselves
how genuinely good their birds were.

Chapter XXII

PIGEON CITY IS ACCLAIMED

PERHAPS it was not alone the fact that the boys had lost most of the honors in the young bird races that created a better atmosphere between them and the rest of the club members. Perhaps the fact that they were older had something to do with it. At any rate, when the Pigeon City boys attended the first of the club meetings, they were received much more cordially than before. At this important meeting a new idea was proposed which resulted in the courses for the whole season being adopted in advance. It was the unanimous opinion that each course should alternate with the next throughout the season. That was one satisfaction to everybody, because now they would all be compelled to train their homers to be versatile—not to rely upon landmarks alone.

After the boys had gone home, "I told you," said one of the old-timers, "that it *was* beginners' luck those kids had been having. I knew they couldn't win any races with birds they bred themselves."

"Of course not," said another. "As I said before, the brains of the bunch left them when the old man died."

"Yes," another agreed, "that put the period on the end of their sentence."

"It was the fine stock they started with that made them successful," said the first. "The old man helped them get that, and with it they easily could win. But their own breeding was no better than most of the rest of ours, if as good."

"Where do you suppose they got the first stock besides what they got from Ross and Collins?" asked another interested member. "Don't you remember those peculiar bands on some of them? There was something funny about it. But that won't bother us any more; they are through, and that is all we need to know."

No matter what the club members said to reassure one another, it was plain that they were not so sure of themselves as they would have their friends believe. Very evidently Pigeon City never ceased to be a menace.

At home, during the winter and spring months, Bud and Dick and Bill had done a lot of thinking and planning. The mating had been executed with every caution and all the wisdom they possessed. Taking into con-

sideration the excellent results of their last
season's matings, which the club members
knew nothing about, they were now sure which
birds would produce the best fliers, and these
were mated. A large number of spry, eagle-
like pigeons filled Pigeon City almost to overflowing, and the boys knew that not a great
many of these would be lost in training flies
or in races. This year, therefore, would have
to be the year in which great chances would
be taken, as a very large number of their birds
must be eliminated. The next fall all three
were planning to go to college, and they
wanted only a few of their very best to be
left at Pigeon City, where the Misses Gardner
would look after them, but thenceforth with
wisdom, rather than with misdirected sentiment.

No longer should Mr. Ross enter any of
their birds; they would risk everything, and
would be fearless. "None but the best for
Pigeon City" had been a motto which had
made pigeon history. Now that motto had
taken on a meaning for the boys which was
even higher than they had believed possible.
"None but the best" meant to them super-
homers. They were going to win every single
race on the calendar, let the club members like
it or not.

Thus the training flies were carried out as usual and with better results than ever before. Fewer birds were lost, and better time was made; more birds returned the first days, and fewer straggled in late. All this was the result of most careful selection over the several years that the boys had been breeding and testing homers.

The breeding season was nearly over, and the fliers' room was already crowded. Both the young and the old birds were given their daily exercise as formerly. While the young ones dearly loved to circle wide and stay up for long periods of time, the old birds took a few turns and then soon returned to their mates and squabs. There were always a few among the old ones that would want to return sooner than rest, which, of course, brought the whole flock down.

Thus the way in which the old birds had to be seasoned was by frequent training flies. Then it became absolutely necessary for them to fly for at least as long as it would take to get home from the point where they had been liberated. This constant training took a great deal of the boys' time after school, and on clear Saturdays until summer came; and then during the summer they had more time. This summer both Bill and Dick found it necessary to spend not a little time on preparation for their college entrance examinations and none of them could go to the country.

"Good old boy," said Bud to Grizzle, as he put him into the carrying cage just before the 100-mile old bird race, "are you going to bring home the bacon this time as you did last? You sweet old racer! Or is one of your sons going to beat you? Or I wonder if that last year's red grizzle will take your number? No, no, never. You are the best."

Grizzle did win, and two of last year's birds of their own breeding came second and third. And once again the club members were all upset.

"Now, look here," said Mr. Ross to a large group of them the very afternoon of the fly, "what's wrong with the boys? I know they have the stock and it will be hard for us to beat them. I never bet before in my life, but next week, on the 250-mile race I'll bet a tidy sum with any man that the boys win. Who'll take it?" Not for some time did any one answer and then the amount he placed was small. It was plain that the boys had sprung a real surprise. And again they won.

Mr. Ross had broken down the barriers. Now a few of the club members began to bet on Pigeon City birds, showing by this that they considered the boys not as outsiders, but as fellow-members in the fullest sense. And those who had won money on their birds felt very friendly indeed toward them. "We owe Mr. Ross a vote of thanks for his sacrifice," the boys all agreed. They could feel the difference in the attitude of at least half of the members, but the remaining half were yet to be won over.

With the winning of the 500-mile race, a few more members became friendly. Now there was not a doubt that the boys had the very best pigeons in the land. Every one was obliged to acknowledge it. Grizzle, who had won the first two races, was known to all. In the 500-mile race he was defeated by his own son, the brown grizzle, who was only a scant two minutes ahead.

Then came the 1000-mile race. Again the boys won, but this time their old favorites were once more withdrawn from competition because the boys felt that the risk was altogether too great. Despite their vows to ship all their birds, at the last minute they could not really bring themselves to say good-by to Grizzle and lazy Red-Check and Whitie. Blackie was sitting on eggs anyway, and some of the others were really too precious. Why risk it?

The time of the race was fast, but it would have been even faster with their best flying against time. The closeness between their birds and those of some of the other club members gave every one courage. But no one realized that Pigeon City's best had not been flown.

Now for the races with the young birds. The boys were winning by wide margins. One day Bill, who had been thinking seriously, asked the other boys to face the facts with him.

"We must either sell at least half of our pigeons or lose them," he said. "Which do you prefer? We can't go away and leave this large number of birds for the Misses Gardner to look after. Thirty or forty is enough. I believe it is best to weed out a lot more. We made a big mistake in holding back so many of our best. I suggest that we give some of the birds to Mr. Ross or somebody, or else sell some."

Something had to be done; that was obvious. They were trying hard to solve that question.

The next meeting of the club was called to decide upon a matter of importance that had arisen. Pigeon City must be represented; it was, and by all three boys.

"Gentlemen," said the president, after calling the meeting to order, "we shall hear the minutes of the last meeting." They were read and approved.

"Is there any report from the treasurer?" This, too, was read and approved.

"Is there any old business to come before the meeting?"

There was. A tall, fine, fatherly-looking man arose in the back of the room. "Gentlemen, I don't really know whether what I have to say is new business or old business, but it doesn't make any difference. It happened last year, and that's why it's old business. It will be news to you, and that's why it's new. I have a confession to make. It is in line with what is coming later because I know why this meeting was called even if you don't, but before our president tells you about it I want to set all of you straight. This is a matter about which you ought to know." He stopped and took a good breath.

"Last year, you will remember that I won a good number of young bird races? You do, of course. Well, here is why and how I won. As a matter of fact, I didn't win a single race, and neither did any one but those three youngsters sitting in the back of the room! It was their birds that did the winning; they

were kind enough to relay the bands on my
birds and let them come home where I put
the bands in my clock. That's exactly how I
won. And if any one doubts, will Mr. Secretary please open his books and turn to his
records? There he will see that the birds that
won are none other than birds that bore on
their legs band numbers assigned to Pigeon
City!"

The secretary shuffled through his record
books, and the members turned excitedly to
each other and whispered or looked about at
the boys, who blushed with well-earned pride.

Finally, the secretary announced, "Mr.
President and Members, Mr. Ross is correct."

"Of course I am correct," answered Mr.
Ross. "I guess we ought to know it, the boys
and I. But don't you see that it took time to
make the transfer of the bands and to get my
birds started for home? So Pigeon City really
had better pigeons than you have given them
credit for."

The members were torn between emotions.
Those who had not come to feel proud of the
boys were angrier than ever, but even then
they could not help feeling a little respect for
these "mystery kids," as they had been affectionately dubbed.

Then Mr. Ross went on, "I am here to pay

my compliments to those three young gentlemen. On the whole I don't think they have
been treated with the courtesy the club owes
them. But I predict that before next week is
over we shall be happy to claim them as our
real friends. Indeed, we shall be proud to
claim them as among the greatest pigeon fliers
who have ever owned a homer. Remember
my words, and consider what I have said."
The club members broke into loud applause,
much to the boys' surprise.

Now there was more whispering, and several
members turned and shook hands with the
boys.

Then an old fancier stood up. "I think
Ross is right. I admit that I have made a
few derogatory remarks myself, and I take
them all back. I am sorry if I have hurt the
boys, and I believe that every member here
will have to take off his hat to our three youngest members, who at the same time own our
best homers."

"But let's wait till the young bird races are
over before we say too much," said a sour old
duffer in the front.

"Bah! Sit down!" yelled several, and not
a few hissed and made catcalls, especially
those who had been fortunate in betting on
the Pigeon City fliers.

The president rapped for order.

"Gentlemen, I am sure that Mr. Ross did not mean to precipitate any such commotion as this by saying what he did. There can be no doubt that the tributes paid to the boys are sincere and well deserved. I want to add mine, but I shall wait to shake hands with them two weeks from to-day, when I shall ask a favor of them: I want to sit with them and watch their birds return."

"What can he mean?" asked Bud of Bill and Dick.

"This meeting," went on the president, "was called to answer a challenge just received from the homing-pigeon clubs within a radius of one hundred miles of here. That includes one in Newark, one in Trenton, two in Manhattan, one in the Bronx, two in Philadelphia, and one at Coney Island. It has been proposed to fly the greatest pigeon race since before the War. We are allowed to enter fifty birds and no more. The distance is to be one thousand miles. Do you accept the challenge? Do you agree to fly for the championship of the Federation of Homing-pigeon Clubs? Because we are the newest club to enter they think we haven't real fliers. But we have, and we'll show them!"

A yell went up from the members. "I move

that we accept," shouted an enthusiast above the noise of the crowd.

"I second the motion," called a boyish voice.

Again the president rapped and order was restored. "It has been moved and seconded that we accept the challenge. Are you in favor? Please signify in the usual manner."

"Aye, aye, aye," they shouted again.

"It is a vote," declared the president. "Gentlemen, the time is short. We must decide to-night upon the birds to be entered."

At once, as though an idea had occurred to them simultaneously, nearly all of those who had been opposed now swung over in favor of the Pigeon City birds. There was such a babel of voices all trying to make suggestions to the president at once that it was some little time before he could restore order. "I would like to hear first of all from one of the owners of Pigeon City. How many birds can you contribute toward the fifty which we are to send? How many birds have you that you would think would stand a good chance of winning?"

After a nudge from each side, Bud stood up. "Sir," he said, "I must tell you that we did not ship our best birds in the last big race. We kept fully fifteen at home because we could not bear to risk losing them, we were so fond of them."

"What, and you won that race with one that you thought was not your best?" asked the president.

"Oh, yes, sir," continued Bud. "Indeed I think that we could send thirty birds if it were for the honor of the club, and I am sure that it would be hard to say which would win." Then Bud turned to the other boys. "What do you say, fellows? Here is a chance to do some more weeding, and we can afford to lose a few. Are you willing?" Yes, they were willing. "Very well," Bud said loudly, so every one could hear, "we are willing to ship all of our very best and will take the risk if it will help the club to win. But you probably don't want so many from one loft. We will send just as many as the rest of the members want."

A cheer went up for these three loyal members. Now they were well within the heart of everybody in the club. They had triumphed.

Chapter XXIII

THE GREAT RACE

WHEN the shipping crates from the club left by truck to join the rest of the crates at the Pennsylvania Station before they started their long railway journey to Florida, thirty birds represented Pigeon City and twenty came from all the rest of the club members together. Without a doubt the greatest homing pigeons in the private lofts of the eastern part of the United States were assembled in the baggage car that pulled out late in the night.

All night long they rode, and all the next day, and part of the night. The weather was warm, and the expressman had opened the doors of the car to keep the birds as cool as possible. In the night the crates were unloaded and taken on trucks down to the very end of the platform and there they were left still sealed, awaiting the dawn of the next day. The station master had been instructed to liberate the birds at the first signs of dawn so they might get as close to home as possible the first day.

He had no trouble in finding enough boys in the vicinity of the station to come and help him open the sides of the crates so that the homers could get away together. There were twenty crates, and ten boys and men on hand. Shortly before dawn the seals were all broken and the locks unfastened; all that remained to do was to open the last latch on each crate and to drop the hinged front.

When the first streaks of dawn appeared on the distant eastern horizon, the men and the boys went to their places. When the light was bright enough for all to see clearly, the station master waved his handkerchief as a signal, noted the exact time, and the race was on. With the dropping of the fronts of the crates the magnificent, powerful homers shot out to the last bird as if there had been powder behind them. Five hundred fliers flew across the field opposite the station and slowly rose higher and higher and began to circle. Not all in one flock—oh, no! These experienced birds knew enough to rely upon no others than themselves. They each knew where to go though they had never been there before. And they went. Some made up their minds more slowly than others, and circled for a

They continued on their journey, flying close to the
sea-coast

while after all the rest had gone. But the men and boys who watched them disappear marveled that nearly all of the fliers headed north and slightly to the east. The station master went inside and sent a telegram stating the exact time of liberation.

The morning was cool for this time of the year. The birds did not seem to try for great altitude. Already they could see a city in the distance—Jacksonville, Florida. It was sound asleep. Most of the birds flew directly over it; nothing there to interest them. Far off to their right the rising sun made a blaze of light reflected from the ocean. They continued on their journey flying close to the sea-coast, and for several hours they were over the State of Georgia. With the rising of the sun they had sought a higher altitude and found it cooler and more comfortable. Brunswick was left behind, and finally another larger city, Savannah, and now they had passed through Georgia and were over the southern part of South Carolina. Some of them stuck to the sea-coast, others left it and took the direct northerly course looking for landmarks and finding none, but guided by that marvelous instinct which we cannot explain. The day was bright but somewhat hazy. Now the fliers had become separated so that few were within sight of each other. Not only had some of the faster fliers gained distance over the rest, but some had flown more to the left and some more to the right, and so they were apart from the others by many miles. As usual, certain birds were well in the lead as was their habit, but there was keen competition among these leaders, without their realizing it.

Far in the lead was a grizzle-colored flier, as usual. Far behind him was a very large red-checked bird, and in between them were many other homers of interest to us. Toward the very front was Miss Ethel's bird with white feathers in its wings. There were several of the original immigrants and some of their squabs; there was a brown grizzle, and a red grizzle, and an almost white one; and there were four coal-black homers. Among them also were dozens of birds from the other clubs, and several from Pigeon City. But it now looked as if that fast-flying grizzle far in the lead had the race pretty well tucked away for his boy owners.

The afternoon was wearing along, and still the steady flapping of the seemingly tireless wings continued, as it bore the birds closer and closer toward home. But instead of old Red-Check being back among the last of the leading birds, he was now well up among the first. Lazy Red-Check, up to his old tricks. He worked well only when he had to, but even then it must be said that he did not give up, as several birds had already done.

The fliers that had followed the coast were losing time; those that were flying straight were cutting off many miles and of course making better time. Now they were crossing North Carolina. Slowly the day was drawing toward its close, and the homers became more and more weary. But now a different bird was leading—none other than Red-Check. With the approach of evening came a new feeling for the best of the Pigeon City fliers. Where would they stay for the night? It was nearly dark.

Just ahead of Red-Check was a large city, Richmond, Virginia. He put on added power and had soon passed over it. There in the distance his far-seeing eyes could observe some pigeons on an old freight-house roof. He hurried toward them and found that there, too, was a horse and mule trough, and to this he went and drank copiously of the refreshing water. And in the faint light he could see a little grain scattered near the tracks where a freight car had been unloaded. He ate a little, and then flew up to the eaves, knocked a smaller common pigeon from his usual perch, and, ruffling up his feathers, made himself comfortable for the night.

But Grizzle, who was not as far as Richmond, where Red-Check had stopped, found himself above the fair-sized town of Petersburg. He, too, could see pigeons below him, and he flew to them. There he found water, but no food; and as it was so dark, he contented himself with the drink and flew up with the strange birds to the side of a public building where he found a place to sleep on a window ledge.

As for the others, they found various places to stay, and not a few were among the pigeons resting in comfortable coops, some of which would be liberated in the morning and some of which would never be allowed their freedom. A few perched on barns while others sat on house roofs. Then some were caught by owls, and a few by cats, but such are the risks that a pigeon fancier takes in sending his birds so far that they will have to stop over night on the way.

Back home, a dozen fanciers had gathered at Pigeon City to see the return. Those who had not owned good enough birds to send were there; the others were watching at their own lofts. By evening these men had gathered, hoping that there might have been a tail wind that by some freak had blown the pigeons along at a speed sufficient to allow them to arrive home the same day. But no such luck. Now at nightfall they took their departure, planning to come early the next morning to see what would happen.

Another day dawned bright and fair, with almost no wind and a slight haze. Grizzle, from his height on the windowsill, opened his eyes and stretched his wings with the first faint rays of light. He waited. He was tired, but not so much so as last night. The other pigeons began to coo to their mates. His mate was at home, he thought, and it made him impatient to get back to Pigeon City. Actually Blackie was a hundred miles behind him, and she too was getting ready to start for home.

Red-Check stretched his wings. He remembered that grain. He thought of the water, and the first thing he did was to fly down for a drink, and then hunt for grain. He gorged himself, eating all he could find. Then he flew up to the roof and looked around. The chill in the air was changing to a warm glow. He liked the feeling of it. The food in his distended crop made him feel lazy. The common pigeons all around were now flying about, looking for food and water, but none flew up, and so he sat there complacently.

Grizzle sought a little food but found none, and almost before it was light he had made a few circles and was up above the housetops and again on his way toward Pigeon City, the home he loved. Soon he too had passed over Richmond, where hundreds of feet below him a lazy red bird reveled in the feeling that his crop was full and he was comfortable. A common pigeon came near him. He cooed and showed his beauty to her by blowing up his crop and dragging his tail. When he came close she flew away, he after her. Just a few flaps of his powerful wings put him abreast of her and this very act of flying soon made him remember that at home were his mate and his squabs; squabs that he had driven out of the nest and perhaps would never recognize as his own. But nevertheless he had raised them, and this very fact had helped to endear Pigeon City to him. So again he was on the way home. But Grizzle was several miles ahead, and so were Whitie, Red-Check's mate, two of the blacks, and two other grizzles, the red and the brown. Red-Check could fly just a trifle faster than any of them, but he was heavy with food. That in itself

was a handicap. Grizzle and some of the rest
were empty and light; Red-Check had over-
eaten, but like the rest he toiled on.

Now familiar landmarks began to appear.
There was that great wide bay of water with
the land on the other side. Straight across
he flew, Grizzle several miles ahead. Just as
on the previous day, the weather slowly became warmer, and the birds flew higher. Soon
they were well across Maryland. No need to
rely upon instinct any longer; the landmarks
were sufficient guide, and all that was necessary was to speed toward home. Home, home,
home! On, on, beat, beat, beat of heart and
wings!

Grizzle was gaining on the rest. Red-Check
was holding his own. But what is that ahead?
A roar of noise. Oh, yes, an aeroplane. It
was coming directly for old Grizzle. He suddenly swerved up and far above the plane.
Yes, he had fooled it, just as he had learned to
do with the hawks that so often had beset his
path. The aeroplane did not catch him; he
continued on his way. And the aviator did
not even see the winged creature that had
helped the builders to improve their planes.

Gradually the food in Red-Check's crop had
disappeared. He was more evenly balanced,
and felt somewhat lighter. He began to be

thirsty, and again put on steam and flew for that water with all his might. The birds were now over New Jersey, flying through the balm of a summer's morning but well up in the air. On, on they sped, looking sometimes to right and left but flying as straight as arrows, seem-

ing to those below just so many specks in the blue.

On the roof of Bud's house three people sat in the little hut, and six more gathered around watching toward the southwest. Below in Pigeon City more men and boys sat eagerly waiting. It was now three o'clock. The Misses Gardner were in their house because they felt so worried about the birds and could almost weep to think of them so far away. Even the boys' parents were on hand to witness the finish. The three fathers had all taken the day off.

"Everything on the outside must look perfectly natural to the birds," warned Bill. "Let every one who wants to watch either sit in the houses and watch through the windows or else come inside the loft; and for goodness' sake be as still as death."

There was no need of the warning. The president and the secretary were there too, and they were as anxious as any to win the race for the honor of the club. They acted as policemen to keep order.

"There's a telephone call for Mr. Jones," called Mr. Hitchcock. "He's the club secretary, isn't he?" Mr. Jones went into the house.

"Hello, is this Mr. Jones, the secretary of the Brooklyn Homing Pigeon Club?" asked the long-distance operator.

"Speaking," said Mr. Jones.

"Hold the line, please." Then after a pause, "Philadelphia wants to speak to Mr. Jones. Ready."

"Hello," said a voice. "This is the secretary of the Philadelphia Pigeon Club. I don't want to crow, but I thought you would like to know that the first Philadelphia bird has just arrived. He is way ahead of the record, and I hope you will tell the clubs near you."

"Thanks, but don't be too sure of yourself. Remember we fellows have a time allowance because you are ninety miles closer than we are. No birds have come here yet, but they will soon. Yes, I'll tell the other clubs near here."

"Well, you won't need to look for birds for an hour, because this one of ours is our champion flier and you haven't anything there that could touch him anyway."

"Time will tell. Thanks. Good-by."

Mr. Jones hurried to the yard. He shouted to the men on the roof. One put his head over the edge. "Birds coming. First one just landed in Philadelphia ten minutes ago. Watch out. I should say they would begin to come in about an hour." Then he went into Pigeon City and told the men in there. The neighbors had heard him shout to the men on the roof and heard what he said, and soon all the windows were full of eager faces. Then Mr. Jones went into Bud's house again and called up the other nearby clubs and passed the news to the secretaries.

On the roof Dick was sitting with a pair of powerful field-glasses, watching. One of the other men had a pair also, and neither let anything escape them.

Red-Check was gaining on Grizzle and the rest. Staten Island, the old familiar Staten Island, was below them. Down the full length they sped, then across the river, and they were over their home city, Grizzle still in the lead, Red-Check second, the brown grizzle and the red grizzle third and fourth, and some blacks bringing up in the rear. Those that had been widely separated were now closer together as their paths all converged on their home. Grizzle was a tired bird; so were all the rest. But Grizzle persevered and—

"Look," cried Dick to the other man with the glasses, "is that one of ours off there? Look sharp. I'm sure it's a pigeon."

Yes, it was a pigeon, but so steady was the flight and so directly toward them it came, that it looked like a speck that did not move.

As they watched, another speck appeared beside it and a little further away. Now those without glasses could see both, and they seemed very close. Closer they came, closer, then they seemed to be dropping. Yes, they were their pigeons!

Dick pressed the button and the light in Pigeon City flashed twice. The men sat as still as ghosts, and Bud and Bill stood ready beneath the trap.

Only a few blocks away now were the two great racers. Now they seemed to draw in their wings and coast and fall slowly.

Zip, one shot over the heads of the spectators.

Zip, shot another. Down to Pigeon City, in through the trap wires dashed the first, and within a few seconds the other.

"Grizzle, you blessed champion!" purred Bud as he held the great homer next to his cheek. "Red-Check, you darling," said Bill. Then putting him down, "Here, you can have your drink and you will never have to leave your home again. We promise."

Again the light flashed. This time it was the brown grizzle, the son of old Grizzle; and soon came the red grizzle, the son of Red-Check. Two clocks had been furnished. Both of these birds were timed, as well as the first two. It had all happened within fifteen minutes after the 'phone message had been received.

"Telephone the Philadelphia club," suggested the president to the secretary, "and tell them they spoke too soon."

"No, I'd rather wait and let them be surprised when they hear the results, just as we were all surprised when these newcomers beat us so badly. The fact that we won won't surprise them nearly so much as learning which club members were responsible."

"Boys," said the president as he shook hands and took his departure, "I have watched your careful efforts with great interest. May everything that you attempt in life succeed as well as your achievements in breeding, raising and flying homers. I hope, however, that you won't all get your eyes on the office of President of the United States at the same time, or Congress will have to amend the Constitution so that we can have three Presidents all at once!"

THE  END